Revit Architecture 2019
For Novices

(Learn By Doing)

CADSoft Technologies

Revit Architecture 2019 for Novices:
Learn By Doing

CADSoft Technologies

CADSoft Technologies

ISBN 978-1-64057-040-5

Online Training Program Offered by CADSoft Technologies

CADSoft Technologies provides effective and affordable virtual online training on various software packages including Computer Aided Design, Manufacturing and Engineering (CAD/CAM/CAE), computer programming languages, animation, architecture, and GIS. The training is delivered 'live' via Internet at any time, any place, and at any pace to individuals as well as the students of colleges, universities, and CAD/CAM/CAE training centers. The main features of this program are:

Training for Students and Companies in a Classroom Setting

Highly experienced instructors and qualified Engineers at CADSoft Technologies conduct the classes under the guidance of Prof. Sham Tickoo of Purdue University Northwest, USA. This team has authored several textbooks that are rated "one of the best" in their categories and are used in various colleges, universities, and training centers in North America, Europe, and in other parts of the world.

Training for Individuals

CADSoft Technologies with its cost effective and time saving initiative strives to deliver the training in the comfort of your home or work place, thereby relieving you from the hassles of traveling to training centers.

Training Offered on Software Packages

CADSoft Technologies provide basic and advanced training on the following software packages:

CAD/CAM/CAE: *CATIA, Pro/ENGINEER Wildfire, SOLIDWORKS, Autodesk Inventor, Solid Edge, NX, AutoCAD, AutoCAD LT, Customizing AutoCAD, AutoCAD Electrical, EdgeCAM, and ANSYS*

Architecture and GIS: *Autodesk Revit (Architecture/Structure/MEP), Autodesk Navisworks, ETABS, Bentley STAAD.Pro, AutoCAD Raster Design, ArcGIS, AutoCAD Civil 3D, AutoCAD Map 3D, Oracle Primavera P6, MS Project*

Animation and Styling: *Autodesk 3ds Max, 3ds Max Design, Autodesk Maya, Autodesk Alias, Pixologic ZBrush, and CINEMA 4D*

Computer Programming: *C++, VB.NET, Oracle, AJAX, and Java*

Table of Contents

Chapter 5: Using the Editing Tools

Chapter 6: Working with Datum Plane and Creating Standard Views

Chapter 7: Using Basic Building Components-II

Chapter 8: Using Basic Building Components-III

Chapter 9: Adding Site Features

Chapter 10: Using Massing Tools

Chapter 11: Adding Annotations and Dimensions

Chapter 12: Creating Project Details and Schedules

Chapter 13: Creating and Plotting Drawing Sheets

Chapter 14: Creating 3D Views

Chapter 15: Rendering Views and Creating Walkthroughs

Preface

Autodesk Revit 2019

Autodesk Revit 2019 is a Building Information Modeling software developed by Autodesk. This software helps AEC professionals to develop high quality and accurate building design.

The **Revit Architecture 2019 for Novices: Learn By Doing** textbook introduces the users to the spectacular realm of one of the most powerful software in the architectural quiver. This textbook is a gateway to power, skill, and competence in the field of architectural and interior presentations, drawings, and documentations.

This textbook is specially meant for professionals and students of architecture and interior design, facilities planners, and CAD professionals who are associated with the building construction and allied fields in the construction industry.

Special emphasis has been laid to explain new concepts, procedures, and methods in Revit by using sufficient text and graphical examples.The accompanying tutorials and exercises, which relate to the real-world projects, help you understand the usage and abilities of the tools available in Autodesk Revit.

The main features of this textbook are as follows:

- **Project-based Approach**
  The author has adopted the project-based approach and the learn-by-doing approach throughout the textbook. This approach helps the users learn the concepts and procedures easily.

- **Real-World Designs as Projects**
  The author has used real-world building designs and architectural examples as projects in this textbook so that the users can correlate them to the real-time designs.

- **Tips and Notes**
  Additional information related to various topics is provided to the users in the form of tips and notes.

- **Learning Objectives**
  The first page of every chapter summarizes the topics that will be covered in that chapter. This will help the users to easily refer to a topic.

Symbols Used in the Textbook

Note

The author has provided additional information to the users about the topic being discussed in the form of notes

Tip

Special information and techniques are provided in the form of tips that helps in increasing the efficiency of the users.

Formatting Conventions Used in the Textbook

Please refer to the following list for the formatting conventions used in this textbook.

- Names of tools, buttons, options, browser, palette, panels, and tabs are written in boldface.

  Example: The **Wall: Architecture** tool, the **Modify** button, the **Build** panel, the **Architecture** tab, the **Properties** palette, the **Project Browser**, and so on.

- Names of dialog boxes, drop-downs, drop-down lists, list boxes, areas, edit boxes, check boxes, and radio buttons are written in boldface.

  Example: The **Options** dialog box, the **Wall** drop-down of the **Build** panel in the **Architecture** tab, the **Name** edit box of the **Name** dialog box, the **Chain** check box in the **Options Bar**, and so on.

- Values entered in edit boxes are written in boldface.

  Example: Enter **Brick Wall** in the **Name** edit box.

- Names of the files are italicized.

  Example: *c14_Club_tut2.rvt*

- The methods of invoking a tool/option from the ribbon, **File** menu, or the shortcut keys are given in a shaded box.

  Ribbon: Architecture Tab > Build > Wall drop-down > Wall
  Shortcut Keys: WA

- When you select an element or a component, a contextual tab is displayed depending upon the entity selected. In this textbook, this contextual tab is referred to as **Modify | (Elements / Components)**.

  Ribbon: Modify | (Elements / Components) > Modify > Move
  Shortcut Key: MV

Naming Conventions Used in the Textbook

Please refer to the following list for the naming conventions used in this textbook.

Tool

If you click on an item in a panel of the ribbon and a command is invoked to create/edit an object or perform some action, then that item is termed as tool.

For example:
Wall: Architectural tool, **Window** tool, **Railing** tool
Filled Region tool, **Trim/Extend to Corner** tool, **Rotate** tool
Link Revit tool, **Detail Line** tool

If you click on an item in a panel of the ribbon and a dialog box is invoked wherein you can set the properties to create/edit an object, then that item is also termed as **tool**, refer to Figure 1.

For example:
Load Family tool, **Materials** tool, **Project Units** tool
Design Options tool, **Visibility/Graphics** tool

Figure 1 Tools in the ribbon

Button

The item in a dialog box that has a 3d shape is termed as **button**. For example, **OK** button, **Cancel** button, **Apply** button, and so on. If an item in a ribbon is used to exit a tool or a mode then that item is also termed as a button. For example, **Modify** button, **Finish Edit Mode** button, **Cancel Edit Mode** button, and so on; refer to Figure 2.

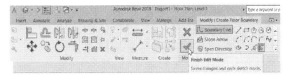

*Figure 2 Choosing the **Finish Edit Mode** button*

Dialog Box

In this textbook, different terms are used for referring to the components of a dialog box. Refer to Figure 3 for the terminology used.

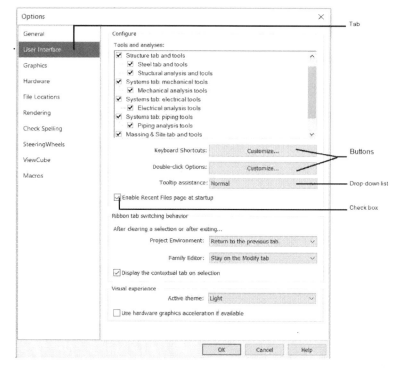

Figure 3 Different components of a dialog box

Drop-down

A drop-down is the one in which a set of common tools are grouped together for performing an action. You can identify a drop-down with a down arrow on it. The drop-downs are given a name based on the tools grouped in them. For example, **Wall** drop-down, **Component** drop-down, **Region** drop-down, and so on, refer to Figure 4.

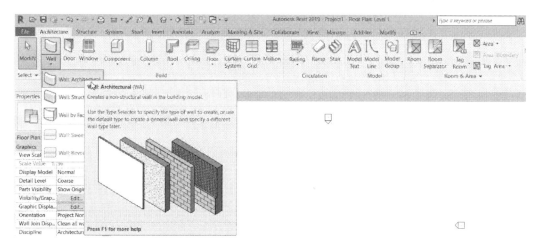

Figure 4 Choosing a tool from a drop-down

Drop-down List

A drop-down list is the one in which a set of options are grouped together. You can set a parameter using an option from this drop-down list. You can identify a drop-down list with a down arrow on it. For example, **Type Selector** drop-down list, **Units** drop-down list, and so on; refer to Figure 5.

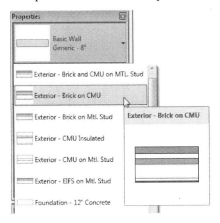

*Figure 5   Selecting an option from the **Type Selector** drop-down list*

Options

Options are the items that are available in shortcut menus, drop-down lists, dialog boxes, flyouts, and so on. For example, choose the **Zoom In Region** option from the shortcut menu displayed on right-clicking in the drawing area; refer to Figure 6.

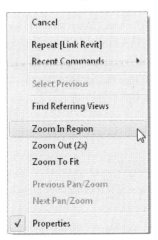

Figure 6   Choosing an option from the shortcut menu

This page is intentionally left blank

Chapter 1

Introduction to Autodesk Revit 2019 for Architecture

Learning Objectives

After completing this chapter, you will be able to:
- *Understand the basic concepts and principles of Revit 2019 for Architecture*
- *Understand different terms used in Revit*
- *Know worksharing using Revit Server*

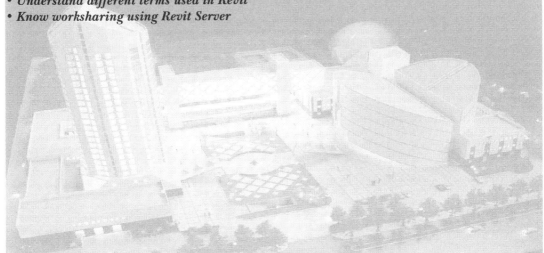

INTRODUCTION

Welcome to the realm of Revit, a powerful building modeler that has changed the outlook of the building industry about computer aided designs. Autodesk Revit is a design and documentation platform that enables you to use a single, integrated building information model to conceptualize, design, and finally document a project. Its integrated parametric modeling technology is used to create the information model of a project, and to collect and coordinate information across all its representations. In Autodesk Revit, drawing sheets, 2D views, 3D views, and schedules are a direct representation of the same building information model. Using its parametric change engine, you can modify a design at any stage of a project. The change in the project is automatically made and represented in all its views, resulting in the development of better designs, along with an improved coordination. The use of Revit provides a competitive advantage and a higher profitability to architects and building industry professionals.

Autodesk Revit AS A BUILDING INFORMATION MODELER

The history of computer aided design and documentation dates back to the early 1980s when architects began using this technology for documenting their projects. Realizing its advantages, information sharing capabilities were developed, especially to share data with other consultants. This led to the development of object-based CAD systems in the early 1990s. Before the development of these systems, objects such as walls, doors, windows were stored as a non-graphical data with the assigned graphics. These systems arranged the information logically, but were unable to optimize its usage in a building project. Realizing the advantages of the solid modeling tools, the mechanical and manufacturing industry professionals began using the information modeling CAD technology. This technology enabled them to extract data based on the relationship between model elements.

In 1997, a group of mechanical CAD technologists began working on a new software for the building industry. The Building Information Modeling (BIM) provided an alternative approach to building design, construction, and management. This approach, however, required a suitable technology to implement and reap its benefits. In such a situation, the use of parametric technology with the Building Information Modeling approach was envisaged as an ideal combination. They developed a software that was suitable for creating building projects. This software was earlier known as Autodesk Revit Architecture, and has now been changed to Autodesk Revit.

Autodesk Revit is a building design and documentation platform in which a digital building model is created using the parametric elements such as walls, doors, windows, and so on. All the building elements have inherent relationship with one another, which can be tracked, managed, and maintained by the computer.

BASIC CONCEPTS AND PRINCIPLES

Autodesk Revit enables you to envisage and develop a building model with actual 3D parametric building elements. It provides a new approach to the architectural thought and the implementation process. In a way, it replicates the way architects conceive a building. For example, 2D CAD platforms mostly use lines to represent all elements, as shown in Figure 1-1. However, in Autodesk Revit, you can create a building model using 3D elements such as walls, floors, doors, and windows, as shown in Figure 1-2.

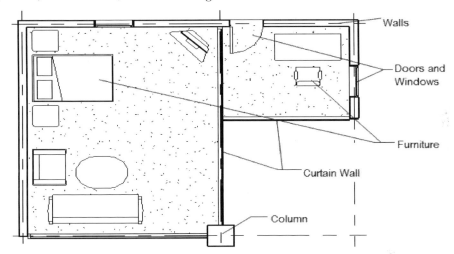

Figure 1-1 *CAD project created using 2D lines and curves*

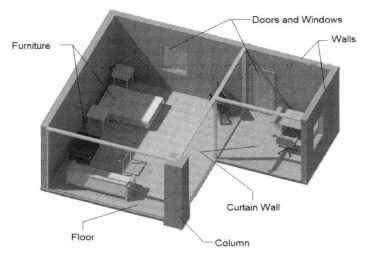

Figure 1-2 *Autodesk Revit project created using parametric building model*

Using these 3D elements, you can visualize the architectural or interior project with respect to its scale, volume, and proportions. This enables you to study design alternatives and develop superior quality design solutions. Autodesk Revit automates routine drafting and coordination tasks and assists in reducing errors in documentation. This, in turn, saves time, improves the speed of documentation, and lowers the cost for users.

STARTING Autodesk Revit 2019

You can start Autodesk Revit 2019 by double-clicking on its shortcut icon located on the desktop. Alternatively, you can start Autodesk Revit 2019 from the taskbar. To do so, choose the **Start** button; a menu is displayed, as shown in Figure 1-3. Choose **Autodesk** and then **Revit 2019**; the interface will be displayed, as shown in Figure 1-4. (For Windows 10)

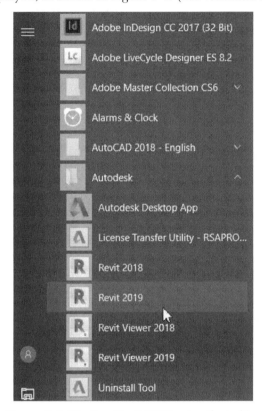

Figure 1-3 Starting Revit 2019 using the taskbar

Note
The path for starting Revit depends on the operating system being used.

The interface screen has three sections: **Projects**, **Families**, and **Resources**. The options in the **Projects** section are used to open an existing project, a new project, and an existing template. The options in the **Families** section are used to open a new or an existing family. You can also invoke the Conceptual Mass environment from this section to create a conceptual mass model.

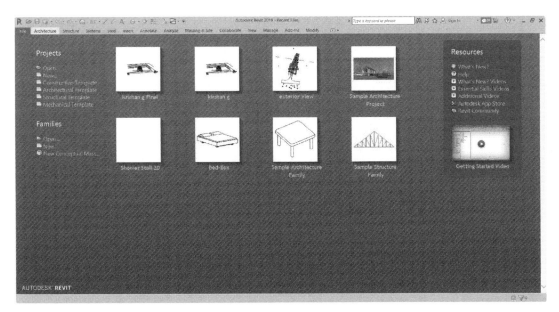

Figure 1-4 *The interface of Autodesk Revit 2019*

In the **Resources** section, you can choose the **What's New?** option to get information about the new tools and features in Revit 2019. In addition, you can choose the **Help** option from the **Resources** section to get help on various tools. When you choose this option, you will be directed to http://help.autodesk.com/view/RVT/2019/ENU/. Also, the **Autodesk Revit 2019** page with the **Welcome to Revit 2019 Learning** area will be displayed. To access information related to additions and enhancements in Revit 2019 release, you can expand the **What's New** node from the left pane and then click on the **What's New** link. On doing so, the **What's New** page will be displayed with various links. You can visit the links to learn about enhancements in Revit 2019.

The **What's New? Videos** option in the **Resources** section is an enhancement in Revit 2019. When you click on this option, you are directed to the **Autodesk Revit 2019** page that has a list of videos of newly added features in Revit. You can click on a link to view the corresponding video.

You can choose the **Essential Skills Videos** and **Additional Videos** options to view the videos related to basic, advance concepts, and modelling in Revit 2019. These videos and their associated information help you to learn about different features and capabilities of the software. Moreover, you can choose the **Autodesk App Store** option to access various add-ons that can be used to enhance the productivity of Revit. On choosing this option, the **Autodesk App Store** page will be displayed. In this page, various links are available as add-ons which can be used in Revit applications. In the **Revit Community** option of the **Resources** section, you can access information related to various communities and their contribution in the form of articles, tutorials, and videos.

In the **Projects** section, choose the **Open** option; the **Open** dialog box will be displayed. Browse to the desired location in the dialog box and select the file. Now, choose the **Open** button to open the file.

To open a new project file, choose the **New** option from the **Projects** section. Alternatively, choose **New > Project** from the **File** menu; the **New Project** dialog box will be displayed. In this dialog box, you can select the desired template from the **Template file** drop-down or you can browse the other template files by using the **Browse** button from the **Template File area**. When you choose the **Browse** button, the **Choose Template** dialog box will be displayed. In this dialog box, make sure the **Project** radio button is selected, and then choose the **OK** button; a new project file will open and the interface screen will be activated.

INTEROPERABILITY OF Autodesk Revit

The models or geometries created in Revit can easily be exported to AutoCAD based programs, such as 3ds Max and Max Design in the DWG file format. This enables you to visualize and create photorealistic exterior and interior renderings for your project designs. You can also transfer drawings from Revit to Google SketchUp to visualize your projects in a better way.

Revit follows a wide range of industry standards and supports various CAD file formats such as DWG, DXF, DWF, DGN, FBX, and SAT. For image files, it supports JPG, TIFF, BMP, PNG, AVI, PAN, IVR, and TGA file formats. Besides these, the formats that are supported by Revit include ODBC, HTML, TXT, gbXML, XLS, and MDB. Revit is compatible with any CAD system that supports the DWG, DXF, or DGN file format. Revit can import the models and geometries as ACIS solids. This enables designers to import models from AutoCAD Architecture and AutoCAD MEP (Mechanical, Electrical, and Plumbing) software and to link and import 3D information to Revit. This feature makes Revit an efficient, user-friendly, and compatible software.

In Revit, you can directly link the files into 3ds Max and load selected views in it. You can also override material in 3ds Max and retain its settings when you reload Revit link file. Also, in 3ds Max, you can add high level of details to the curved objects to make them smooth. Microstation is interoperable with Revit. Therefore, the Microstation files can be imported to the Revit project. In addition to this, mapping functionality for levels, lines, line weights, patterns, and texts and fonts is added to export DGN workflow.

BUILDING INFORMATION MODELING AND Autodesk Revit

Building Information Modeling (BIM) is defined as a design technology that involves creation and use of coordinated, internally consistent, and computable information about a building project in design and construction. BIM covers spatial relationships, geographic information, quantities, and properties of building components. Using this technology, you can demonstrate the entire life cycle of a building project starting from the process of construction, facility operation, and information about quantities and shared properties of elements. BIM enables the circulation of virtual information model from the design team to contractors and then to the owner, thereby adding changes and their knowledge to update the model at each stage of transfer. The ability to keep information up-to-date and make it available in an integrated digital environment enables the architects, owners, builders, and engineers to have clear vision of the project before the commencement of actual construction. It enables them to make better and faster decisions as well as to improve the quality and profitability of projects. Autodesk Revit is a specially designed platform based on BIM. Revit is the best example of the BIM technology. Revit's parametric model represents a building as an integrated database of coordinated information. In Revit, change anywhere is change everywhere. Any change made in your project at any stage is reflected in the entire project, and also, due to the parametric behavior of elements, the project is updated automatically according to the changes made anywhere in the project. Also, the integration of Revit with the available in-built commercial tools such as solar studies, material takeoffs, greatly simplifies the project design and reduces the time consumed by these analyses, thereby enabling faster decision making.

Autodesk Revit 2019 HELP

Autodesk Revit provides help to easily understand various tools and methods used in it. In Autodesk Revit 2019, you can access online help documentation. To access the help feature, click on the down arrow on the right of the **InfoCenter**; a flyout will be displayed. Next, choose the **Help** option, as shown in Figure 1-5. Various options to access the help are discussed next.

Figure 1-5 A drop-down menu displaying help options

Using the Revit 2019 Help

You can access Autodesk Revit 2019 help when you are online. To do so, choose the **Help** tool from the **InfoCenter**; the **Autodesk Revit 2019** page will be displayed, as shown in Figure 1-6. In this page, there are several tabs that contain information of help topics. These tabs are useful to understand the basic concepts of Revit.

*Figure 1-6 The **Revit Help** page*

WORKSHARING USING REVIT SERVER

Worksharing is a method of distributing work among team involved in a project, and accomplishing it within the stipulated period of time. In worksharing, each person involved in the project is assigned a task that has to be accomplished by proper planning and by coordinating with the other members of the team.

In a large scale building project, worksharing helps in finishing a project in time and meeting the quality requirements that are set during the process. Generally, in a large scale building project, worksharing is based on the specialization of work. The professionals such as structural engineers, architects, interior architects, and MEP engineers are involved in their respective fields to accomplish the project. So, the distribution of work at the primary stage is made on the basis of the area of specialization. Each professional has his own set of work to perform for the accomplishment of the project.

You can apply server-based worksharing with the help of Revit Server as it is a server based application. Revit Server uses a central server and multiple local servers for collaborating across a Wide Area Network (WAN). The central server hosts the central model of a workshared project and remain accessible to all the team members over the Wide Area Network. Similarly, the local server is accessible to all team members in a Local Area Network (LAN). The local server hosts a local updated copy of the central model. In the Worksharing environment, the team members are not aware of the local server, as it is transparent in their daily operations. Refer to Figure 1-7 for the network model of Revit Server.

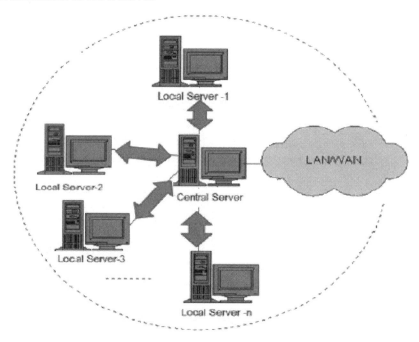

Figure 1-7 *The network model of Revit Server*

In Worksharing environment, a team member starts working on the local model of the central model. The local model will be saved in the computer of the team member. As the team member works, the local server requests updated information from the central model on the central server using available network capacity to transfer the data over the WAN. The updated version of the model is stored on the local server, so the updates are readily available when a team member requests them.

Chapter 2

Starting an
Architectural Project

Learning Objectives

After completing this chapter, you will be able to:
- *Start a new architectural project*
- *Set units of various measurement parameters of a project*
- *Understand the concept of snaps, dimensions, and object snaps*
- *Save a project*

INTRODUCTION

In Revit, you can work on structural, architectural, and MEP (Mechanical, Electrical and Plumbing) projects on a single platform. The chapters in this textbook are specially written for professionals in architectural and space design field. In this chapter, you will learn about the tools and the processes involved in starting up a new architectural project

STARTING A NEW ARCHITECTURAL PROJECT

Shortcut Key:	CTRL+N
File menu:	New > Project

In Revit, a project is considered as a single database that contains all information related to building design. Starting from geometry to construction data, each project file contains complete information of the building design. In a building design, the three dimensional models drawn using this software are called BIM (Building Information Model). BIM is a process involving the generation and management of digital representation of physical and functional features of different infrastructure elements.

To start an architectural project, choose **New > Project** from the **File** menu, as shown in Figure 2-1. On doing so, the **New Project** dialog box will be displayed, as shown in Figure 2-2. Using this dialog box, select an existing *.rte* template file format that can be used in the new project.

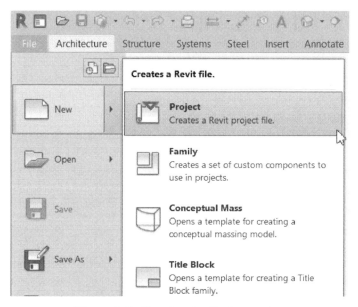

Figure 2-1 *Choosing the **Project** option*

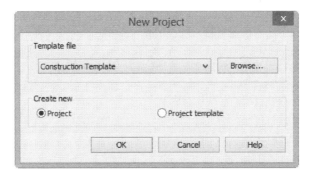

*Figure 2-2 The **New Project** dialog box*

A template file can be defined as a template which has various project parameters such as units and views, already saved in it. On using the template file, the new project file will adopt the same parameters as the template file. The difference between a template file and a project file is that the template file has a *.rte* extension, whereas the project file has a *.rvt* extension. You can either select any of the template files provided in Revit or create your own file. Any project file can be saved as a template file.

In the **New Project** dialog box, select the desired template file from the drop-down list in the **Template file** area. By default, the **Construction Template** option is selected. To select a different template file which is not available in the drop-down list, choose the **Browse** button. On doing so, the **Choose Template** dialog box will be displayed. In this dialog box, browse to the **US Imperial** or **US Metric** folder, select a template file, and then choose the **Open** button; the selected template file will be added to the drop-down list in the **Template file** area.

In the **Create new** area of the **New Project** dialog box, two radio buttons will be displayed: **Project** and **Project template**. The **Project** radio button is selected by default. As a result, you will work on a new project. Alternatively, if you select the **Project template** radio button, you will work on a new project template.

> **Note**
> *If you select the **None** option from the drop-down list in the **New Project** dialog box, a new project file will be created without a template file but with the default settings of Revit.*

PROJECT UNITS

Ribbon:	Manage > Settings > Project Units
Shortcut Key:	UN

 Units are important parameters in a project. While installing Revit, you are prompted to set the default unit as Imperial (feet and inches) or Metric (millimeter). The default selection of units helps you open project with the specified/selected unit system. However, you can change the default unit set system. To set units, choose the **Project Units** tool from the **Settings** panel of the **Manage** tab; the **Project Units** dialog box will be displayed, as shown in Figure 2-3. Project units are grouped into six disciplines: **Common**, **Structural**, **HVAC**, **Electrical**, **Piping**, and **Energy**. Each discipline has a set of measurement parameters. You can select any of these disciplines from the **Discipline** drop-down list of this dialog box. In this drop-down list, the **Common** option is selected by default. As a result, various measurement parameters such as **Length**, **Area**, **Volume**, **Angle**, **Slope**, **Currency**, and **Mass Density** will be displayed in the **Project Units** dialog box. The **Format** column in the dialog box displays the current unit format for the corresponding parameter. You can preview and select the possible digit grouping and decimal separators from the **Decimal symbol/digit grouping** drop-down list located at the lower left corner of the dialog box, refer to Figure 2-3. The options for settings measurement units are discussed next.

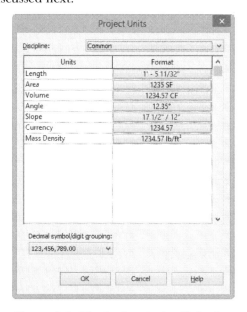

Figure 2-3 *The* ***Project Units*** *dialog box*

Length Unit

To assign a unit for measuring the lengths of building elements in your project, click on the **Format** column corresponding to the **Length** parameter; the **Format** dialog box will be displayed, as shown in Figure 2-4. This dialog box displays different units of length and their settings. You can select the desired unit from the **Units** drop-down list in the dialog box. After selecting the desired unit, you can specify the rounding value for the selected unit. To do so, select the desired option from the **Rounding** drop-down list in the **Format** dialog box. Note that by default, the **Rounding increment** edit box in the **Format** dialog box is inactive. To make it active, select an option from the **Units** drop-down list and then select the **Custom** option from the **Rounding** drop-down list. The default value in the **Rounding increment** edit box is 1. You can change this value by entering a value in this edit box. Similarly, the **Unit symbol** drop-down list will be inactive for the **Feet and fractional inches**, **Fractional inches**, and **Meters and Centimeters** options of the **Units** drop-down list. From the **Unit symbol** drop-down list, you can select the measurement symbol that will be added to the unit of length. For example, you can select '**m**' as the measurement symbol after all metric length measurement. In case, you select **Feet and fractional inches** from the **Units** drop-down list in the **Format** dialog box, then you need to select the **Suppress spaces** check box to remove spaces in the dash when a length string is expressed in feet and fractional inches to denote a particular measurement.

Tip
*While selecting a rounding value from the **Rounding** drop-down list in the **Format** dialog box, you should consider the extent of detailing that may be required for the project. For projects that require too much detailing, a lower rounding value may be set. This parameter, however, can be modified at any stage during the project development.*

*Figure 2-4 The **Format** dialog box*

Area Unit

To assign a unit for measuring the areas of building elements, click on the **Format** column for the **Area** parameter; the **Format** dialog box will be displayed. In this dialog box, you can set the unit for measuring an area by selecting an option from the **Units** drop-down list. This drop-down list contains various options such as **Square feet**, **Square meters**, **Acres**, and so on. By default, the **Square feet** option is selected in this drop-down list. The settings for rounding, rounding increment, and units can be done by selecting the desired option from the respective drop-down list and edit boxes.

Volume Unit

The units for volume can be set similar to that of the length and area. You can set the unit for the volume measurement by selecting any of the options from the **Units** drop-down list in the **Format** dialog box of the **Volume** parameter.

Angle Unit

The units for angle can be set by using the **Units** drop-down list in the **Format** dialog box of the **Angle** parameter.

Slope Unit

To specify the unit for the slope measurement, click in the **Format** column for the **Slope** parameter; the **Format** dialog box will be displayed. In this dialog box, you can specify the desired unit settings by selecting the required option from the **Units** drop-down list. The default selected option for the Imperial unit setting in the drop-down list is **Rise / 12"**.

Currency Unit

The currency unit is used to set the unit of currency for its usage in the cost and estimation schedules. To set the unit of currency, invoke the **Project Units** dialog box and then choose the button displayed in the **Format** column corresponding to the **Currency** parameter; the **Format** dialog box will be displayed. From this dialog box, you can select the required type of currency symbol from the **Unit symbol** drop-down list.

Mass Density Unit

The mass density of building elements is required for structural analysis. In Revit, you can assign a unit for measuring mass density. To assign the unit of mass density, invoke the **Project Units** dialog box. In the **Format** column of this dialog box, choose the button corresponding to the **Mass Density** parameter; the **Format** dialog box will be displayed. In this dialog box, you can select different units from the **Units** drop-down list. Also, you can assign a unit symbol for the selected unit. To do so, click on the **Unit symbol** drop-down list and then select any of the options displayed.

Tip
*As soon as you change the units and choose the **OK** button to close the **Format** dialog box, the numbers and units shown for each measurement parameter in the **Project Units** dialog box are modified to the new settings. You can modify these settings and format them as per your requirement.*

Note
*You can format the display of units represented on the screen using the **Project Units** dialog box. The actual values for these units in the project may be different. For example, if you set the wall length rounding to the nearest 1', the wall may show this rounded value, but the actual length of the wall might be in fractional feet.*

SNAPS TOOL

Ribbon:	Manage > Settings > Snaps

The **Snaps** tool is one of the most productive tools available while creating and editing elements in a building model. This tool represents the ability of the cursor to snap or jump to the preset increments or specific object properties of various elements such as endpoint, midpoint, and so on. Invoke the **Snaps** tool from the **Settings** panel of the **Manage** tab; the **Snaps** dialog box will be displayed, as shown in Figure 2-5. This dialog box has three areas: **Dimension Snaps**, **Object Snaps**, and **Temporary Overrides**. These areas are discussed next.

Note
*The settings in the **Snaps** dialog box are applied to all the projects opened in the session but are saved in the project you are working on.*

Tip
The values that you will enter for dimension snapping should be set based on the scale and the amount of detailing required for the project. You may set smaller increments for working on a detail or a small portion of a building.

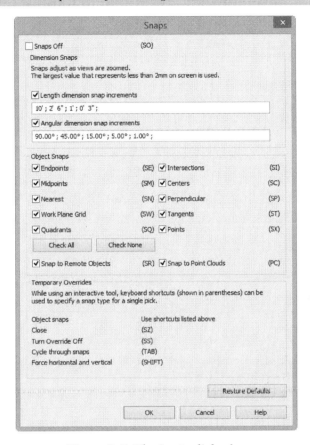

*Figure 2-5 The **Snaps** dialog box*

Dimension Snaps Area

In this area, you can set increments for placing elements or components in a project view. You can set increments for the length and angle dimensions. To set the increment of length dimension, select the **Length dimension snap increments** check box, if it is not selected by default, and then enter the increment values in the edit box below it. The default values entered in this edit box are: **10'** ; **2'6"** ; **1'** ; **0'3"**; for Imperial (**3000** ; **750** ; **300** ; **75** ; for Metric). Note that every incremental value is separated by a semicolon (;). You can also set increments by typing the values separated by a semicolon. For example, to create an interior layout plan in which the length of the partitions is in 5'(1524 mm) modules, counter top width is 2'(609.6 mm), and the thickness of partitions is 4"(101.6 mm), you can enter the values for the dimension snaps as 5'; 2';4" for Imperial (1524; 609.6;101.6 for Metric). This will enable the cursor to move in these increments and help create the layout with relative ease.

In the **Dimension Snaps** area, snap increments for angular dimensions can be set by selecting the **Angular dimension snap increments** check box and then entering suitable values in the edit box below this check box. This setting is quite useful for projects that have radial geometry.

Tip
*The **Snaps** tool is frequently used not only while creating various building elements but also while editing and placing them. By efficiently using this feature, you can improve the performance and accuracy of your project besides making modeling much simpler.*

Object Snaps Area

In the **Object Snaps** area, you can specify various object snaps for using them in a project. Object snapping refers to the cursor's ability to snap to geometric points on an element such as endpoints, midpoint, perpendicular, and so on. It is useful for creating and editing elements. The advantage of using object snapping is that you can locate the appropriate point on a drawing object. When enabled, the appropriate object snap is displayed as soon as the cursor is near to an element. For example, it is virtually impossible to pick the exact endpoint to start a wall from an endpoint of an already drawn wall. But when you enable the **Endpoints** object snap, the cursor automatically jumps or snaps to the endpoint of this wall. This helps to start the new wall from the endpoint. This, besides making the drawing accurate, later helps in adding dimensions to the project.

Note
The object snapping works only with the objects that are visible on the screen. A tooltip, with the same name as the object snap, is also displayed when you bring the cursor close to the snap point.

Various object snap modes available in the **Object Snaps** area are: **Endpoints**, **Midpoints**, **Nearest**, **Work Plane Grid**, **Quadrants**, **Intersections**, **Centers**, **Perpendicular**, **Tangents**, **Points**, **Snap to Remote Objects**, and **Snap to Point Clouds**.

The use of each object snap corresponds to its respective name. The **Work Plane Grid** snap option enables you to snap to a point on a reference plane already defined in the model. For example, you can place a furniture component exactly on the floor by snapping to the floor level reference plane. You can snap to the object that is closest to the cursor using the **Snap to Remote Objects** option. You can also snap points of a point cloud data object by selecting the **Snap to Point Clouds** check box. Each object snap mode has a geometrical shaped marker to identify it from the other object snaps. For example, the endpoint object snap is indicated by a square, midpoint by a triangle, nearest by a cross, and so on. To use an object snap mode, move the cursor over the object. You will notice a marker that appears as you move it close to the snap point. To select the appropriate snap point, click when the corresponding marker or tooltip is displayed.

In Revit, all the enabled object snaps work simultaneously. You can turn off all the snap options including the dimension snaps and object snaps by clearing the **Snaps Off** check box located at the top of the **Snaps** dialog box. Alternatively, you can type **SO** on the keyboard to turn them off and on while using a tool. The **Check All** and **Check None** buttons can be used to enable or disable the object snaps, respectively.

Temporary Overrides Area

The options in the **Temporary Overrides** area provide you the alternative of overriding snaps setting for a single use only. For example, if you have not selected the **Endpoints** object snap in the **Snaps** dialog box and you want to use this option while working with a tool, you need not open the **Snaps** dialog box and set this option. You can instead type the shortcut, **SE** to temporarily activate the endpoint object snap. Once you have used this object snap option, snapping to the endpoint is automatically turned off.

You can toggle between various object snap options available at the same location using the TAB key on the keyboard. Hold down the SHIFT key to create the elements vertically or horizontally. This restricts the movement of the cursor in the orthogonal directions only. Once you release the SHIFT key, the cursor resumes its movement in all directions. You can select the **Snaps Off** check box to disable all types of snapping.

SAVING A PROJECT

You must save your work before closing a project or exiting the Revit 2019 session. You have the option of saving the project file in a permanent storage device, which may be a hard disk or a removable disk. Also, you must save your work at regular intervals to avoid loss due to any error in the computer's hardware or software.

Saving the Project File

File menu:	Save As > Project
Shortcut Key:	CTRL+S

To save the project file to the desired location, choose **Save As > Project** from the **File** menu; the **Save As** dialog box will be displayed, as shown in Figure 2-6. Alternatively, you can save the project file by choosing the **Save** button from the **Quick Access Toolbar**. In the **Save As** dialog box, the **Save in** drop-down list displays the current drive and path in which the project file will be saved. The list box below the **Save in** drop-down list shows all the folders available in the current directory. The **File name** edit box can be used to enter the name of the file to be assigned to the project. The **Places List** area on the left of the **Save As** dialog box contains shortcuts for the folders that are frequently used.

Figure 2-6 The **Save As** *dialog box*

 Tip
The selection of a large number of backup files for storing may lead to consumption of resources in the hard disk.

Using the Options Button

You can use different features for saving a file by choosing the **Options** button from the **Save As** dialog box. On choosing this button, the **File Save Options** dialog box will be displayed, as shown in Figure 2-7. Using the **Maximum backups** edit box from this dialog box, you can specify the maximum number of backup files that you need to store for the project. In Revit, by default the non-workshared projects have three backup files and the workshared projects have twenty backup files. The options in the **Thumbnail Preview** area enable you to specify the image to be used as the preview of the project file that can be used at the time of opening a project file. You can specify the view of the model to be used as a preview image by selecting an option from the **Source** drop-down list. The **Active view/sheet** is the default option for previewing a project file. For example, to make the **Floor Plan: Level 1** the preview image, select it from the drop-down list. Whenever you select this project file, the preview will always show the **Floor Plan: Level 1**, irrespective of the last active view.

*Figure 2-7 The **File Save Options** dialog box*

Select the **Regenerate if view/sheet is not up-to-date** check box to see the preview with the latest modifications. Selecting this check box will update the preview image on closing the project file.

Note

*Revit updates the preview image continuously. Therefore, selecting the **Regenerate if view/sheet is not up-to-date** check box can consume considerable resources.*

Using the Save Tool

Once the project is saved using the **Save As** tool, you do not need to re-enter the file parameters to save it again. To save a project to a location, choose the **Save** tool from the **File** menu. While saving the project for the first time, the **Save As** dialog box is displayed, even if you invoke the **Save** tool. Alternatively, you can save your project by choosing the **Save** button from the **Quick Access Toolbar**. As you save your project file, Revit 2019 updates it automatically without prompting you to re-enter the file name and path.

TUTORIALS

In the tutorials of this chapter, you will work on three projects: an apartment complex, a club building and a residential building. However, some portions of these three projects will be completed in the tutorials and the rest will be given as exercises that need to be completed by the students themselves. The tutorials and exercises form a sequence, and therefore, to complete these projects, you need to complete both the tutorials and exercises in the previous chapters. The following tutorials will familiarize you with the tools and concepts discussed in this chapter such as starting Revit, opening a new project, setting units, setting snaps, saving, and closing a project.

Tutorial 1   Apartment 1

In this tutorial, you will create a new project file for the *Apartment 1* project with the following parameters.   **(Expected time: 15 min)**

1. Template file-
                For Imperial   *default.rte*
                For Metric   *DefaultMetric.rte*
2. Project Units-
        For Imperial   **Feet and fractional inches** Rounding- **To the nearest 1/2"**
        For Metric   **Millimeters**   Rounding- **0 decimal places**
3. Length dimension snap increment-
        For Imperial   **5' ; 2'6"; 3"; 0'1/2"**
        For Metric   **1500 ; 750 ; 75 ; 10**
4. File name to be assigned-
        For Imperial   *c02_Apartment1_tut1.rvt*
        For Metric   *M_c02_Apartment1_tut1.rvt*

The following steps are required to complete this tutorial:

a. Start Revit 2019 session.
b. Use the template file for the project.
        For Imperial   *default.rte*
        For Metric   *DefaultMetric.rte*
c. Set the project units using the **Format** dialog box.
        For Imperial   **Feet and fractional inches**
        For Metric   **Millimeters**
d. Set the length dimension snap increment using the **Snaps** dialog box.
        For Imperial   **5'; 2'6"; 3"; 0'1/2"**
        For Metric   **1500 ; 750 ; 75 ; 10**
e. Set **Endpoint**, **Midpoint**, **Nearest**, **Perpendicular**, **Work Plane Grid**, **Snap to Remote Objects**, and **Intersection** as the object snaps in the **Snaps** dialog box.
f. Save the project using the **Save As** tool.
        For Imperial   *c02_Apartment1_tut1.rvt*
        For Metric   *M_c02_Apartment1_tut1.rvt*
g. Close the project.

Starting Revit 2019

1. Start Revit 2019 by choosing **All Programs > Autodesk > Revit 2019 > Revit 2019** from the **Start** menu (for Windows 7). Alternatively, double-click on the Revit 2019 icon on the desktop. As a result, the program is loaded and the user interface screen is displayed.

2. Choose **New > Project** from the **File** menu; the **New Project** dialog box is displayed.

Using the Template File

To use the template file for the project, you need to access the appropriate folder and then select the required template file.

1. In the **New Project** dialog box, choose the **Browse** button from the **Template file** area; the **Choose Template** dialog box is displayed showing a list of the template files available in the **US Imperial** folder.

2. In the **Choose Template** dialog box, select the **default** template file from the **US Imperial Folder** (**DefaultMetric** template file from the **US Metric** folder), refer to Figure 2-8 and then choose the **Open** button; the **Choose Template** dialog box closes and the selected template file is applied to the new project.

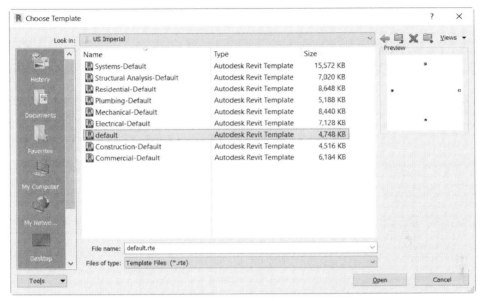

Figure 2-8 The Choose Template dialog box with the default file selected

3. Ensure that the **Project** radio button is selected in the **New Project** dialog box. Next, choose the **OK** button from the dialog box; the *default.rte* (for Metric *DefaultMetric.rte*) template file is loaded. Notice that the **Project Browser** now shows different levels and views that have already been created in the selected template.

Setting Units

To set units for the project,

1. Choose the **Project Units** tool from the **Settings** panel of the **Manage** tab; the **Project Units** dialog box is displayed.

2. Click on the **Format** column next to the **Length** parameter; the **Format** dialog box is displayed.

3. In the **Format** dialog box, select the required option from the **Units** drop-down list, if not selected by default.
    For Imperial   **Feet and fractional inches**
    For Metric   **Millimeters**

4. Click on the **Rounding** drop-down list in this dialog box and select the required option, as shown in Figure 2-9.

    For Imperial   **To the nearest 1/2"**
    For Metric   **1 decimal place**

5. Choose the **OK** button; the **Project Units** dialog box is displayed. Choose the **OK** button; the specified units are applied and the dialog box is closed.

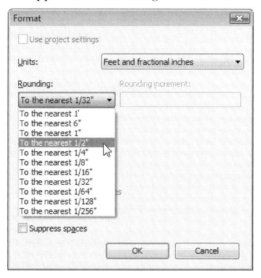

Figure 2-9 Selecting the To the nearest 1/2" option in the Format dialog box

Setting the Dimension and Object Snaps

To set the dimension and object snaps, use the **Snaps** tool. These settings are based on the type of the project and the amount of detailing required.

1. Choose the **Snaps** tool from the **Settings** panel of the **Manage** tab; the **Snaps** dialog box is displayed. In the **Length dimension snap increments** edit box, enter the following values.

    For Imperial   **5'; 2'6"; 3"; 0'1/2";**
    For Metric   **1500 ; 750 ; 75 ; 10;**

2. In the **Object Snaps** area, clear the **Quadrants**, **Centers**, **Tangents**, and **Points** check boxes. Leave other check boxes selected. Choose the **OK** button; the settings are applied and the **Snaps** dialog box is closed.

3. Select the **Temporary Dimensions** option from **Manage > Settings > Additional Settings** drop-down list; the **Temporary Dimension Properties** dialog box is displayed. In this dialog box, ensure that the **Centerlines** radio button is selected in the **Walls** and **Doors and Windows** areas.

4. Choose the **OK** button; the **Temporary Dimension Properties** dialog box is closed.

Saving the Project

The project parameters set in the previous steps are an integral part of the project file. To save this project file with these settings, use the **Save** tool.

1. Choose the **Save** tool from the **File** menu; the **Save As** dialog box is displayed.

2. In this dialog box, browse to the *C* drive and then create a folder with the name **rvt_2019**.

3. Open the *rvt_2019* folder and then create a sub-folder with the name *c02_revit_2019_tut*. Next, open the created folder and save the file with the following name, refer to Figure 2-10.
   For Imperial   *c02_Apartment1_tut1*
   For Metric   *M_c02_Apartment1_tut1*
   Notice that the **Files of type** drop-down list shows **Project Files (*.rvt)** as the default option.

4. Choose the **Save** button to save the project with the name *c02_Apartment1_tut1.rvt*. The project is saved at the specified location.

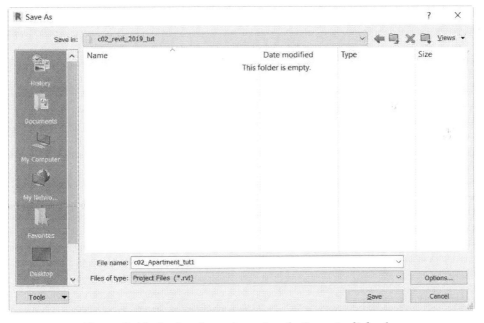

*Figure 2-10 Saving the project using the **Save As** dialog box*

Closing the Project

1. To close the project, choose the **Close** option from the **File** menu.

Tutorial 2	Club

In this tutorial, you will create a new project file for the *Club* project using the following project parameters.   **(Expected time: 15 min)**

1. Template file-
       For Imperial   *Commercial-Default.rte*
       For Metric   *DefaultMetric.rte*
2. Project Units-
       For Imperial   **Feet and fractional inches**
       For Metric   **Millimeters**
3. Length dimension snap increment-
       For Imperial   **10';2'6";1'; 0'3"**
       For Metric   **3000; 750; 300; 75**
4. Object snaps to be set- all available object snaps
5. File name to be assigned-
       For Imperial   *c02_Club_tut2.rvt*
       For Metric   *M_c02_Club_tut2.rvt*

The following steps are required to complete this tutorial:

a. Start Revit 2019 session.
b. Use the template file by accessing the **US Imperial** templates folder.
       For Imperial   *Commercial-Default.rte*
       For Metric   *Construction-DefaultMetric.rte*
c. Set the project units using the **Project Units** dialog box.
       For Imperial   **Feet and fractional inches**
       For Metric   **Millimeters**
d. Set the length dimension snap increment in the **Snaps** dialog box.
       For Imperial   **10';2'6";1'; 0'3"**
       For Metric   **3000 ; 750 ; 300 ; 75**
e. Select the option for rounding.
       For Imperial   **To the nearest 1/4"**
       For Metric   **2 decimal places**
f. Enable all the object snaps using the **Snaps** dialog box.
g. Save the project using the **Save As** tool.
       For Imperial   *c02_Club_tut2.rvt*
       For Metric   *M_c02_Club_tut2.rvt*
h. Close the project.

Starting Autodesk Revit 2019 and Opening a New Project

1. Start a new Autodesk Revit 2019 session by double-clicking on the Revit 2019 shortcut icon on the desktop. On doing so, the user interface screen is displayed. In case, the Revit 2019 session is already running, this step can be ignored and the project file can be opened directly.
2. Choose **New > Project** from the **File** menu; the **New Project** dialog box is displayed.

Using the Template File

As given in the project parameters, you need to use the *Commercial-Default.rte* template file for Imperial and *DefaultMetric.rte* in this project.

1. In the **New Project** dialog box, choose the **Browse** button; the **Choose Template** dialog box is displayed. In this dialog box, select the **Commercial-Default** template file from the **US Imperial** templates folder (**DefaultMetric** from US Metric folder) and then choose **Open**; the selected template file is assigned to the project. Next, choose **OK**; the template file is loaded.

    Notice that the **Project Browser** now shows several levels that are preloaded in the template file.

Setting Units

You can set units for various measurement parameters using the **Project Units** dialog box.

1. Choose the **Project Units** tool from the **Settings** panel of the **Manage** tab; the **Project Units** dialog box is displayed, as shown in Figure 2-11.

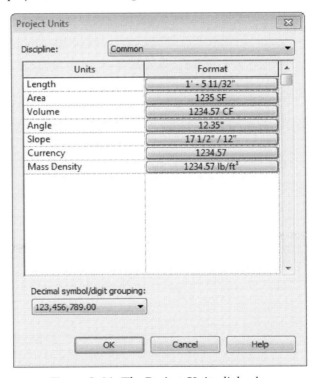

Figure 2-11 The Project Units dialog box

2. Click on the **Format** column next to the **Length** unit; the **Format** dialog box is displayed. In this dialog box, make sure that the **Feet and fractional inches** option for Imperial or **Millimeters** option for Metric (default option) is selected in the **Units** drop-down list.
3. Next, select the required option from the **Rounding** drop-down list.
    For Imperial   **To the nearest 1/4"**
    For Metric   **2 decimal places**

4. Choose **OK** to return to the **Project Units** dialog box. Next, choose the **OK** button to apply the settings and return to the user interface screen.

Setting Dimensions and Object Snaps

In this section of the tutorial, you need to access and modify the settings in the **Snaps** dialog box. Further, you need to specify the dimension snap increment and enable all the object snap options.

1. Choose the **Snaps** tool from the **Settings** panel of the **Manage** tab; the **Snaps** dialog box is displayed, as shown in Figure 2-12.

Figure 2-12 The Snaps dialog box

2. In the **Object Snaps** area, ensure that all the check boxes for snapping are selected.

3. In the **Length dimension snap increments** edit box, enter the following values.
    For Imperial   **10'; 2'6"; 1'; 0'3";**
    For Metric   **3000 ; 750 ; 300 ; 75**
    Choose the **OK** button; the settings are applied and the **Snaps** dialog box is closed.

4. Choose the **Temporary Dimension** option from **Manage > Settings > Additional Settings** drop-down list; the **Temporary Dimension Properties** dialog box is displayed. In this dialog box, ensure that the **Centrelines** radio button is selected in the **Walls** and **Doors and Windows** areas.

5. Choose the **OK** button; the **Temporary Dimension Properties** dialog box is closed.

Saving the Project

In this section, you will save the project and the settings using the **Save** dialog box.

1. Choose **Save As > Project** from the **File** menu; the **Save As** dialog box is displayed.

2. Browse to the *c02_revit_2019_tut* sub-folder in the *rvt_2019* folder and enter the required file name in the **File name** edit box. Notice that the **Files of type** drop-down list shows **Project Files (*.rvt)** as the default option.

    For Imperial   **c02_Club_tut2**
    For Metric   **M_c02_Club_tut2**

3. Choose the **Save** button to save the project. The project is saved at the specified location.

Closing the Project

1. Choose the **Close** option from the **File** menu.

EXERCISES

Exercise 1   Apartment 2

Create a new project file for the *Apartment 2* project with the following parameters:

(Expected time: 15 min)

1. Template file-
    For Imperial   **default.rte**
    For Metric   **DefaultMetric.rte**
2. Project Units-
    For Imperial   **Feet and fractional inches**
    For Metric   **Millimeters**
3. Length dimension snap increment-
    For Imperial   **5'; 2'6"; 3"; 0'1/2"**
    For Metric   **1500 ; 750 ; 75 ; 10**
4. File name to be assigned-
    For Imperial   *c02_Apartment2_ex1.rvt*
    For Metric   *M_c02_Apartment2_ex1.rvt*

Exercise 2   Elevator and Stair Lobby

Create a new project file for the *Elevator and Stair Lobby* project with the following parameters: **(Expected time: 15 min)**

1. Template file-
    > For Imperial   **default.rte**
    > For Metric   **DefaultMetric.rte**
2. Project Units-
    > For Imperial   **Feet and fractional inches**
    > For Metric   **Millimeters**
3. Length dimension snap increment-
    > For Imperial   **5'; 1'; 3"; 0'1"**
    > For Metric   **1500 ; 300 ; 75 ; 25**
4. File name to be assigned-
    > For Imperial   *c02_ElevatorandStairLobby_ex2.rvt*
    > For Metric   *M_c02_ElevatorandStairLobby_ex2.rvt*

Chapter 3

Creating Walls

Learning Objectives

After completing this chapter, you will be able to:
• *Understand the concept of walls*
• *Understand the properties of walls*

CREATING A BUILDING PROJECT

In Revit, the term 'project' comprises not only the physical building model but also its associated documentation such as drawings, views, schedules, areas, and so on. The first step in creating a project is to create the building model. In Autodesk Revit, you can create it using the following two methods:

Method 1:   Create a building model using individual building elements such as walls, windows, doors, floors, roofs, and so on.

Method 2:   Create a conceptual mass of a building model using the massing tools and conceptualize the overall building shape and volume before working with individual elements.

Tip
You can also use a combination of above two methods. You can generate a building mass using the massing tools and then convert it into a building model with individual building elements using the building maker tools.

The selection of method depends on different project parameters such as project magnitude, building shape, building technology, current documentation stage of a project, industry parameters, and so on. The use of the massing tools to create a building geometry and the usage of individual building components to develop a building model will be described later.

Autodesk Revit provides you with several tools to add individual building elements such as wall, floor, roof, and so on for creating a building model. Several predesigned element types have been provided for each building element in Autodesk Revit libraries. You have the flexibility to either use the predesigned element types or create your own element type to create a building model.

Sequence of Creating a Building Model

The sequence of using building elements for creating a building model depends on various parameters such as building type, building volume, building shape, and so on. For most of the building projects, the sequence given below may be adopted.

Step 1: Start the model by creating the exterior walls of the building at Level 1 (lowest level).

Step 2: Create interior walls at the desired locations.

Step 3: Add doors and windows to the exterior and interior walls at the desired location.

Step 4: Add the floor to the building model.

Step 5: Add the roof to the building model.

Step 6: Add the structural or architectural grid and structural elements.

Step 7: Add stand-alone components such as furniture items and plumbing fixtures.

Step 8: Add text and annotations to different spaces.

Step 9: Create dimensions for different parameters of the project.

Step 10: Create project details and documentation.

Step 11: Create the rendered 3D views and walkthrough.

In Revit, each building element is considered a three-dimensional parametric entity. This means, on adding elements to the model, you also add the related information and specification about the elements. One of the most important elements in a building model is the wall. It defines the basic spatial arrangement of the building that acts as the host for doors and windows.

Understanding Wall Types

Autodesk Revit provides you with several predefined wall types such as **Exterior, Interior, Retaining, Foundation, Curtain,** and **Stacked Wall,** based on their usage.

Exterior Wall Type

This category constitutes the wall types that are primarily used for generating the exterior skin of the building model. It has predefined wall types such as **Brick on CMU, Brick on Mtl. Stud, CMU Insulated,** and so on.

Interior Wall Type

The interior walls are used as the interior partitions in a building project. These walls are non-bearing in character. The predefined interior walls provided in Autodesk Revit have a dry wall construction with a metal stud frame and varying thickness.

Retaining Wall Type

As the name suggests, the primary function of the retaining walls is to retain the earth. You can either use the retaining walls provided in the program or set the function of any wall type as retaining. For example, you can select a wall from the drawing and select **Retaining - 12" Concrete** for Imperial (**Retaining 300mm Concrete** for Metric) from the **Properties** palette. On doing so, the current wall type will be changed for retaining wall.

Foundation Wall Type

The walls that form the foundation or substrate of the main building structure belong to this category. To create a foundation wall, the **Foundation - 12" Concrete** option for Imperial (**Foundation- 300mm Concrete** for Metric) is provided as the predefined foundation wall type in the **Properties** palette.

Curtain Wall Type

These wall types have predefined curtain walls or screen walls that consist of panels and mullions.

Stacked Wall Type

A stacked wall is a wall that is made of different types of walls stacked vertically on top of each other.

This software provides you with the flexibility of creating your own wall type. The walls that you will create can have different parameters which can be modified, depending on their usage. In Revit, you can create both architectural and structural walls. An architectural wall does not contain analytical properties like the structural walls. In the next section, various techniques to create and modify architectural walls are discussed.

TUTORIALS

The following tutorials are designed to familiarize you with the concepts of invoking the **Wall: Architectural** tool, selecting the wall type, modifying the wall properties, using the sketching tools, and sketching a wall with the given parameters.

All the files used in the tutorials can be downloaded from the CADSOFT website. These files are compressed in zip file format and are required to be extracted before using them in the tutorials. The path of the files is as follows: *Textbooks > Civil/GIS > Revit Architecture > Revit Architecture 2019 For Novices*. For example, the tutorial file, *c02_Apartment_tut1.rvt* that is used in Tutorial 1 of Chapter 3 is compressed in the *c02_rvt_2019_tut.zip file*.

Tutorial 1	Apartment 1

In this tutorial, you will create the exterior walls of a two-room apartment based on the sketch plan shown in Figure 3-1. The dimensions have been given only for reference and are not to be used in this tutorial. The project file and the parameters to be used for creating the exterior walls are given next.   **(Expected time: 30 min)**

1. Project file-
        For Imperial   *c02_Apartment_tut1.rvt*
        For Metric   *M_c02_Apartment_tut1.rvt*
2. Exterior wall type- **Basic Wall: Exterior - Brick on Mtl. Stud**.
3. Location line parameter- **Wall Centerline**; Top Constraint- **Up to Level 2.**

    The following steps are required to complete this tutorial:

a. Open the *Apartment 1* project file created in Tutorial 1 of Chapter 2.
b. Invoke the **Wall**: **Architectural** tool from the ribbon.
c. Select the exterior wall type **Exterior - Brick on Mtl. Stud** from the **Properties** dialog box.
d. Modify **Top Constraint- Up to level: Level 2** and **Location Line - Wall Centerline**
    as wall properties using the **Properties** palette, refer to Figure 3-2.
e. Invoke the **Line** sketching tool and then sketch the exterior walls based on the given
    parameters, refer to Figures 3-3 through 3-10.
f.   Save the project using the **Save As** tool.
        For Imperial   *c03_Apartment1_tut1.rvt*
        For Metric   *M_c03_Apartment1_tut1.rvt*
g. Close the project.

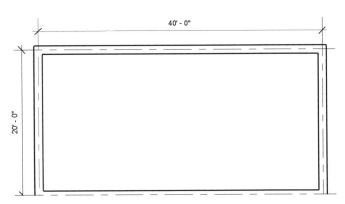

Figure 3-1 *Sketch plan for creating exterior walls for the Apartment 1 project*

Opening the Project File

Choose **Open > Project** from the **File** menu and open the *c02_Apartment1_tut1.rvt* *(M_c02_Apartment1_tut1.rvt for Metric)* project file. You can also download this file from *http://www.cadsofttech.com*. The path of the file is as follows: *Textbooks > Civil/GIS > Revit Architecture > Revit Architecture 2019 For Novices*.

Invoking the Wall: Architectural Tool and Selecting the Wall Type

To start sketching the wall, you must invoke the **Wall: Architectural** tool from the ribbon and select the wall type to be used **(Exterior - Brick on Mtl. Stud** in this case).

1. Invoke the **Wall: Architectural** tool from **Architecture > Build > Wall** drop-down; the **Modify | Place Wall** tab is displayed.

2. In the **Type Selector** drop-down list of the **Properties** palette, select the **Exterior - Brick on Mtl. Stud** wall type.

Modifying Properties of the Exterior Wall

After selecting the wall type, you need to modify the instance properties of the wall type using the **Properties** palette.

Note
The default.rte or (DefaultMetric.rte for Metric) template file used for this project has two predefined levels: **Level 1** *and* **Level 2**.

1. In the **Properties** palette, ensure that the **Location Line** parameter has **Wall Centerline** as the default value. Click on the column adjacent to the **Top Constraint** instance parameter; a drop-down list is displayed. Select **Up to level: Level 2** from this drop-down list, and choose the **Apply** button, as shown in Figure 3-2.

 Tip
*If the **Properties** palette is not displayed in the User interface screen by default, select the **Properties** check box from **View > Windows > User-Interface** drop-down.*

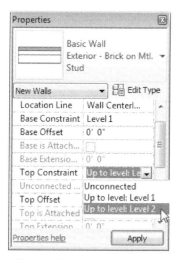

Figure 3-2 *Setting the **Top Constraint** parameter using the **Properties** palette*

Sketching the First Exterior Wall Segment

To sketch a wall, you need to choose an appropriate sketching tool from the **Draw** panel in the **Modify | Place Wall** tab. The exterior walls of the given sketch of the *Apartment 1* project can be created using the **Rectangle** tool. You will however use the **Line** tool to learn and understand the usage of this tool for sketching the straight walls.

1. Ensure that the **Line** tool is chosen in the **Draw** panel in the **Modify | Place Wall** tab and the **Chain** check box is cleared in the **Options Bar**.

2. Ensure that the **Allow** option is selected in the **Join Status** drop-down list.

3. Click between the four inward arrow keys to specify the start point of the first wall segment. Next, move the cursor toward the right hand side. On doing so, a wall segment starts from the specified point with temporary dimension appearing on it. The dimension changes dynamically as you move the cursor. This shows the length of the wall segment at any given location of the cursor.

4. Right-click in the drawing area; a shortcut menu is displayed. Choose the **Zoom In Region** option from the shortcut menu and zoom into the area to get a closer view of the sketched wall segment, as shown in Figure 3-3 (for zooming techniques, refer to Chapter 2- Starting an Architectural Project).

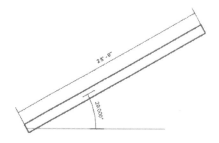

Figure 3-3 *The temporary dimensions displayed on the wall*

5. Move the cursor on the horizontal axis such that a dashed line appears at the central axis of the wall segment, as shown in Figure 3-4. Notice the two-sided arrow attached to the endpoint of the wall. This indicates that the wall segment being sketched is horizontal. A tooltip indicating the horizontal alignment is also displayed with two-sided arrow.

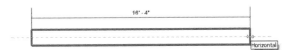

Figure 3-4 *Sketching a horizontal wall segment*

6. Move the cursor to the right until the temporary dimension shows a value more than 40'- 0"(12192 mm), as shown in Figure 3-5. Click at this location as the endpoint of the wall segment and press ESC twice; the wall is created. Note that, if the dimension is not displayed, you need to click on the created wall to display the dimension. Press ESC.

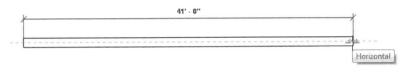

Figure 3-5 *The sketched horizontal wall with its controls*

Note
*You can create a wall of exactly 40'0"(12192 mm) length using the dimension snaps set in the **Snaps** dialog box. The only purpose of creating a wall of length more than the desired length is to explain how to modify the length of the sketched wall to the exact value.*

Modifying the Length of the Sketched Exterior Wall

You will now modify the length of the sketched wall to the actual dimension, as given in the *Apartment 1* sketch.

1. Select the created wall and click on its temporary dimension; an edit box appears showing the current dimension of the wall segment.

2. Enter **40' (12192 mm)** in the edit box, as shown in Figure 3-6 and then press ENTER; the length of the wall is modified to 40'0"(12192 mm). Press ESC to exit the **Modify | Walls** tab.

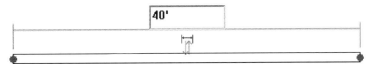

Figure 3-6 *Modifying the length of a wall segment using temporary dimensions*

Tip
*To exit the current tool, you can also right-click and choose **Cancel** from the shortcut menu displayed.*

Note

*By default, the exterior faces of the walls drawn from the left to right are on the upper face, and those drawn from top to bottom are on the right face. Similarly, the exterior faces of the walls drawn from right to left are on the lower face, and those drawn from the bottom to top are on the left side. Hence, you can minimize the use of the **flip** tool by sketching the walls in the appropriate direction.*

Sketching Other Exterior Wall Segments

In this section, you need to create other exterior wall segments using the **Endpoint** object snap tool.

1. Choose the **Wall: Architectural** tool from **Architecture > Build > Wall** drop-down. Now, bring the cursor close to the right endpoint of the first wall segment. When the cursor shows a square box at the endpoint (indicating the **Endpoint** object snap), as shown in Figure 3-7, click to specify the start point of the second wall segment.

Figure 3-7 Starting a second exterior wall segment using the
***Endpoint** object snap option*

2. As you move the cursor, wall starts to get created dynamically, with one end attached to the specified point and the other end attached to the cursor. Move the cursor vertically downward. A dashed vertical line is visible inside the wall segment. Now, enter **20'0"(6096 mm)** as the value of the length; an edit box is displayed with the dimension that you have entered, as shown in Figure 3-8. Press ENTER; the second wall segment is sketched exactly to 20'0"(6096 mm) length.

Notice that the intersection of the first and second wall segments has been intuitively filled or completed.

Figure 3-8 Creating the second exterior wall segment

3. To draw the third wall segment, select the **Chain** check box from the **Options Bar**.

4. Move the cursor close to the endpoint of the second wall segment and click when the endpoint object snap is displayed. On doing so, the third wall segment starts from this specified point. Move the cursor horizontally toward the left. Now, hold the SHIFT key while moving the cursor.

Notice that the cursor can now move only in the orthogonal directions (in the horizontal and vertical direction). When the length of the wall segment is around 40'0"(12192 mm), a vertical dashed line originates from the start point of the first wall segment. The alignment line shows the point on the third wall segment that is in plumb with the first point. An intersection snap symbol indicated by an X appears at this point, as shown in Figure 3-9.

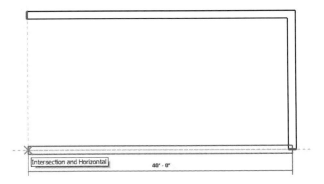

Figure 3-9 *Creating the third wall segment*

5. Click to specify the location of the endpoint of the third wall segment when the intersection snap symbol is displayed.

6. As you have enabled the **Chain** option, the next wall segment automatically starts from the last specified point. Move the cursor vertically upward and enter **25'(7620 mm)**, as shown in Figure 3-10, and then press ENTER. The fourth wall segment is created.

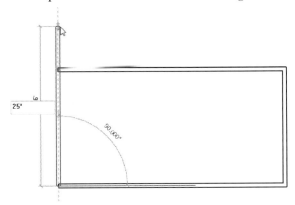

Figure 3-10 *Sketching the fourth exterior wall segment*

7. Press ESC twice to exit the **Wall: Architectural** tool.

Note
The purpose of creating a wall more than the desired length is only to explain how to stretch the wall to the exact length.

Stretching the Wall Segment

You will now stretch the wall segment to change its length to the desired dimension by using the drag controls.

1. Select the fourth wall segment to display its controls. The two blue dots at its two endpoints are the drag controls. Move the cursor near the upper dot; the color of the drag control symbol changes, as shown in Figure 3-11. Press and hold the left mouse button at this point and drag the cursor vertically downward and bring it close to the start point of the first wall segment. On doing so, the endpoint object snap is displayed at the intersection of two walls and the tooltip shows **Endpoint and Vertical**.

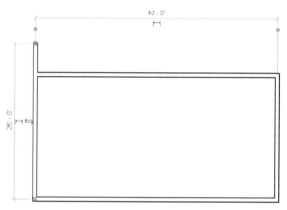

Figure 3-11 Using the drag control to modify the length of wall

2. Release the left mouse button at the intersection point and click; the first and fourth wall segments are joined at the corner with their ends completed.
    Note that if these wall segments do not join at the corner on releasing the left mouse button, you need to click at their intersection.

3. Press ESC to remove the wall segment from the selection set. The external wall profile is completed for this tutorial, as shown in Figure 3-12.

Figure 3-12 The completed exterior wall profile

Saving the Project

In this section, you will save the project file using the **Save As** tool.

1. Choose **Save As > Project** from the **File** menu; the **Save As** dialog box is displayed. Create a folder with the name **c03_revit_2019_tut** and then save the file with the name **c03_Apartment1_tut1** (**M_c03_Apartment1_tut1**).

2. Choose the **Close** option from the **File** menu; the file is closed.

| **Tutorial 2** | **Club** |

Create the exterior walls of the club building and it's sketch plan is shown in Figure 3-13. The dimensions have been given only for reference and are not to be used in this tutorial. The parameters to be used for creating the exterior walls of the club building are given next.

(Expected time: 30 min)

1. Project file-
    For Imperial   *c02_Club_tut2.rvt*
    For Metric   *M_c02_Club_tut2.rvt*
2. Exterior wall type- **Exterior - Split Face and CMU on Mtl. Stud**.
3. Unconnected height of walls- **15'0" (4572 mm)**.
4. All inclined walls are at 45-degree to the horizontal axis.

The following steps are required to complete this tutorial:

a. Open the project file.
    For Imperial   *c02_Club_tut2.rvt*
    For Metric   *M_c02_Club_tut2.rvt*
b. Invoke the **Wall: Architectural** tool.
c. Select the exterior wall type:
    For Imperial   **Exterior - Split Face and CMU on Mtl. Stud**
    For Metric   **Exterior - Brick on Mtl. Stud**
d. Set the unconnected height to **15'0"** or **4572mm**.
e. Change the **Location Line** parameter to **Finish Face: Exterior**, refer to Figure 3-13.
f. Select the **Line** sketching option and sketch the inclined wall profile using the **Chain** option, refer to Figures 3-15 through 3-21.
g. Use the **Center-ends Arc** sketching option to create the curved wall, refer to Figures 3-22 and 3-24.
h. Save the project using the **Save As** tool.
    For Imperial   *c03_Club_tut2.rvt*
    For Metric   *M_c03_Club_tut2.rvt*
i. Close the project.

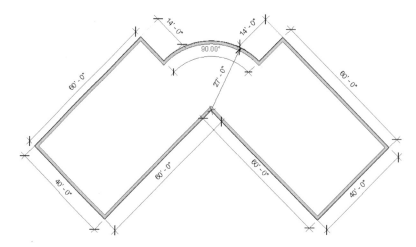

Figure 3-13 Sketch plan for the Club project

Opening an Existing Project

Choose **Open > Project** from **File** menu and open the *c02_Club_tut2.rvt* (*M_c02_Club_tut2.rvt* for Metric) project file created in Tutorial 2 of Chapter 2. You can also download this file from *http://www.cadsofttech.com*. The path of the file is as follows: *Textbooks > Civil/GIS > Revit Architecture > Revit Architecture 2019 For Novices*.

Invoking the Wall: Architectural Tool and Selecting the Wall Type

First, you will invoke the **Wall: Architectural** tool from the ribbon and then select the specified exterior wall type, as given in the project parameters.

1. Choose the **Wall: Architectural** tool from the **Architecture > Build > Wall** drop-down; the **Modify | Place Wall** tab is displayed.

2. In the **Properties** palette, select the required option from the **Type Selector** drop-down list.
    For Imperial   **Exterior - Split Face and CMU on Mtl. Stud**
    For Metric   **Exterior - Brick on Mtl. Stud**

Modifying Properties of the Exterior Wall

Next, you will use the **Properties** palette to modify the unconnected height to 15'0" or 4572mm. The dimensions given in the sketch are exterior wall face dimensions. Therefore, you need to set the **Location Line** parameter to **Finish Face: Exterior**.

1. In the **Properties** palette, click in the value field corresponding to the **Unconnected Height** parameter and replace the current value with **15'0" (4572mm)**.

2. Click in the value field of the **Location Line** parameter and select the **Finish Face: Exterior** option from the drop-down list displayed, as shown in Figure 3-14. Choose the **Apply** button to accept the specified values.

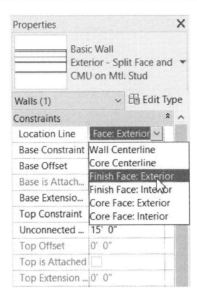

Figure 3-14 *Selecting the **Finish Face : Exterior***
*option for the **Location Line** parameter*

Sketching the Inclined Exterior Walls

Start creating the exterior wall profile by first sketching the inclined walls in a sequence such that the exterior face of the wall is on the external side. You need to select the **Chain** check box to sketch the continuous wall profile. Once you have created the first inclined wall, the other parallel and perpendicular walls can easily be created using the alignment lines and different object snaps options.

1. To create the straight wall, choose the **Line** tool in the **Draw** panel of the **Modify | Place Wall** tab, if it is not chosen by default.

2. In the **Options Bar**, select the **Chain** check box, if it is not selected. Also, select the **Allow** option from the **Join Status** drop-down list.

3. To start sketching the first inclined wall segment, click inside the four arrow keys in the drawing window and move the cursor upward toward the right and then move it to an inclination such that the angle subtended at the horizontal axis is 45 degrees.

4. Enter the value **14' (4267 mm)** to specify the length of the first wall segment; the value is displayed in the edit box, as shown in Figure 3-15. Press ENTER to create the first wall segment of the specified length.

5. As the **Chain** check box is selected in the **Options Bar**, the second wall segment will start from the last specified point. Now, move the cursor downward toward the right and right-click to invoke the shortcut menu. Next, choose **Snap Overrides > Perpendicular** from the shortcut menu displayed; the perpendicular snap symbol appears at the end of the wall. Enter **60'(18288 mm)**, see Figure 3-16; a wall is created perpendicular to the first inclined wall.

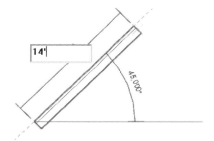

Figure 3-15 *Sketching the first inclined wall segment*

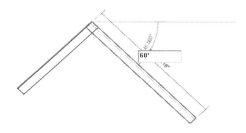

Figure 3-16 *Sketching the second inclined wall segment*

6. Similarly, for creating the next wall, move the cursor downward to the left and choose the perpendicular snap override as in step 5. Enter **40'(12192 mm)** as length, as shown in Figure 3-17. Now, press ENTER to create the third inclined wall.

7. To create the next wall, move the cursor upward toward the left and invoke the perpendicular snap override as in step 5. Enter **60' (18288 mm)** as the length of the wall segment and press ENTER to create the fourth inclined wall segment, as shown in Figure 3-18.

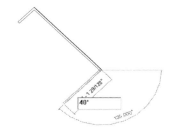

Figure 3-17 *Sketching the third inclined wall segment*

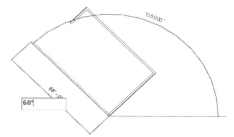

Figure 3-18 *Sketching the fourth inclined wall segment*

8. Similarly, create the fifth inclined wall segment of 60'(18288 mm) length, as shown in Figure 3-19.

9. Next, create the connected wall segment of 40'(12192 mm) length, as shown in Figure 3-20.

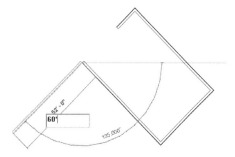

Figure 3-19 *Sketching the fifth inclined wall segment*

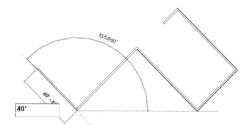

Figure 3-20 *Sketching the sixth inclined wall segment*

10. Now, create the next two wall segments of lengths 60'(18288 mm) and 14'(4267 mm) to complete the inclined wall exterior profile, as shown in Figure 3-21.

Figure 3-21 The sketched inclined wall exterior profile

11. Press the ESC key to discontinue the wall at this point and finish sketching the inclined walls.

Sketching the Curved Exterior Wall

Next, you will sketch the curved exterior wall profile based on the given parameters. You need to use the **Center-ends Arc** tool to create the curved wall segment.

1. Choose the **Center-ends Arc** tool in the **Draw** panel of the **Modify | Place Wall** tab. Move the cursor in the drawing window and click on the outer intersection of the inclined walls to specify the center of the curved wall, refer to Figure 3-22 .

2. Move the cursor near the endpoint of the last sketched inclined wall segment. When 135-degree is displayed as the angular dimension, enter the value **27' (8100 mm)** as the radius of the curved wall and press ENTER, as shown in Figure 3-22. On doing so, the curved wall with the specified radius starts from the specified point.

 Note
While tracking the wall, if the perpendicular or other snapping symbol does not appear, you can right-click and choose **Snap Overrides**; *a cascading menu will be displayed. Choose any snapping option from the cascading menu. On doing so, the desired snapping symbol will appear for the specified point or action.*

3. Move the cursor toward the right and click when the cursor snaps to the endpoint of the inclined wall, as shown in Figure 3-23. Now, press ESC twice to complete the exterior wall profile, as shown in Figure 3-24.

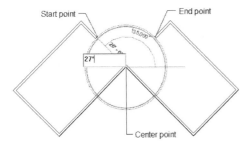

Figure 3-22 Starting the curved wall segment

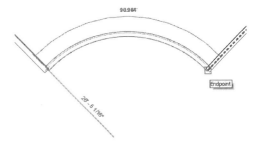

Figure 3-23 Completing the curved wall segment

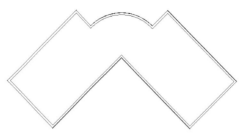

Figure 3-24 *Completed layout of the exterior walls for the Club project*

4. Choose the **Default 3D View** tool from **View > Create > 3D View** drop-down; a 3D view of the building model is displayed, as shown in Figure 3-25.

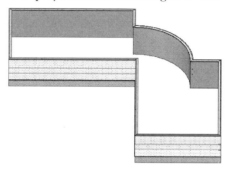

Figure 3-25 *3D view of the completed exterior wall profile*

5. From **View Control Bar**, choose the **Visual Style** button; a flyout is displayed. Choose the **Shaded** option from the flyout.

6. Under the **Floor Plans** head in the **Project Browser**, double-click on **Level 1** to return to the plan view.

Saving the Project

In this section, you will save the project file using the **Save As** tool.

1. Choose **Save As > Project** from **File** menu; the **Save As** dialog box is displayed. Now, browse to the folder **c03_revit_2019_tut** and enter **c03_Club_tut2** (**M_c03_Club_tut2** for Metric) and choose **Save**.

2. Choose the **Close** option from the **File** menu; the file is closed.

EXERCISES

Exercise 1   Apartment 2

Create the exterior and interior walls of the *Apartment 2*, based on Figure 3-26. The thick walls are the exterior walls and the thin walls are the interior walls. The dimensions and texts are not to be added. The project parameters for this exercise are given next.

(Expected time: 30 min)

1. Project file -
   For Imperial   *c02_Apartment2_ex1.rvt.*
   For Metric   *M_c02_Apartment2_ex1.rvt.*
2. Exterior wall type- **Exterior - Brick on Mtl. Stud**.
3. Interior wall type-
   For Imperial   **Basic Wall: Interior - 5" Partition (2-hr)**.
   For Metric   **Basic Wall: Interior - 135mm Partition (2-hr)**.
4. Height of the wall- **Top Constraint - Up to Level 2**.
5. Location line parameter for the exterior walls- **Wall Centerline**.
6. Name of the file to be saved-
   For Imperial   **c03_Apartment2_ex1**
   For Metric   **M_c03_Apartment2_ex1**

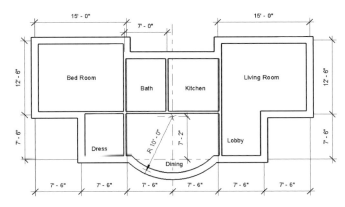

Figure 3-26 *The sketch plan for creating the exterior and interior walls for the Apartment 2 project*

Exercise 2   Elevator and Stair Lobby

Create the exterior walls of the *Elevator and Stair Lobby* project, based on Figure 3-27. Do not add dimensions or texts as they are given only for reference. The project parameters for this exercise are given next.   **(Expected time: 30 min)**

1. Project file -
   For Imperial   *c02_ElevatorandStairLobby_ex2.rvt*
   For Metric   *M_c02_ElevatorandStairLobby_ex2.rvt*
2. Exterior wall type - **Basic Wall Exterior Brick on Mtl. Stud**.
3. Height of the wall - **Top Constraint- Up to Level 2**.
4. Location line parameter - **Wall Centerline**.
5. Name of the file to be saved -
   For Imperial   **c03_ElevatorandStairLobby_ex2**.
   For Metric   **M_c03_ElevatorandStairLobby_ex2**.

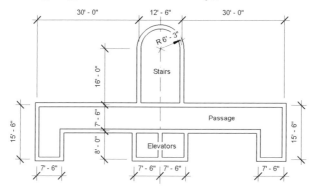

Figure 3-27 *Sketch plan for creating the exterior walls for the Elevator and Stair Lobby proje*

5. Location Line- **Wall Centerline**.
6. Inclined walls are parallel to the external walls and perpendicular to each other.
7. Name for saving the file-
   For Imperial   **c03_residential_wall_ex4**.
   For Metric   **M_c03_residential_wall_ex4**.

Chapter 4

Using Basic Building Components-I

Learning Objectives

After completing this chapter, you will be able to:

• *Understand the concept of doors*
• *Add doors to the exterior and interior walls*
• *Add windows to a building model*

ADDING DOORS IN A BUILDING MODEL

A door is one of the most frequently used components in a building model. It helps in accessing various exterior and interior spaces in a project. Autodesk Revit provides a variety of predefined door types. You can access these door types by using the options from the **Type Selector** drop-down list of the **Properties** palette. You can also load other door types from the **US Imperial** or **US Metric** folder. A wall acts as a host element for doors. This means that a door can be placed only if there exists a wall. When you add a door to a wall, Autodesk Revit intuitively creates an opening in it. The procedure for adding doors to a building model is described next.

Adding Doors

You can add doors to a building model by using the **Door** tool. You can invoke this tool from the **Build** panel, as shown in Figure 4-1. Alternatively, you can type **DR** to invoke this tool.

Figure 4-1 *Invoking the **Door** tool from the **Build** panel*

To add a door, invoke the **Door** tool; the **Modify|Place Door** tab will be displayed in the ribbon. Select the desired door type from the **Type Selector** drop-down list in the **Properties** palette and the instance properties of the door will be displayed.

ADDING WINDOWS TO A BUILDING MODEL

Windows form an integral part of any building project. Autodesk Revit provides several in-built window types that can be easily used and added to a building model. Like doors, windows are also dependent on the walls that act as their host element.

Adding Windows

Ribbon:	Architecture > Build > Window
Shortcut Key:	WN

In Autodesk Revit, you can add windows to a building model by using the **Window** tool. To do so, invoke the **Window** tool from the **Build** panel of the **Architecture** tab, The **Modify|Place Window** tab will be displayed. In this tab, select the window type from the **Type Selector** drop-down list in the **Properties** palette.

TUTORIALS

Tutorial 1   Apartment 1

In this tutorial, you will add doors and windows to the apartment project file created in Tutorial 3 of Chapter 3. Refer to Figure 4-2 for adding these elements. The dimensions and the text have been given for reference and are not to be added. The project file name and parameters to be used are given next.   **(Expected time: 30 min)**

1. Project file-
    For Imperial   *c03_Apartment1_tut3.rvt*
    For Metric   *M_c03_Apartment1_tut3.rvt*

2. Door types to be used
    For Imperial   1- **Single - Flush: 30"x 84"**
                       2 and 3- **Door - Interior - Single - 4 - Panel - Wood - 36"x 84"**
                       4- **Door-Exterior-Single-Two_lite - 48" x 96"**
                       Door openings- **Passage Opening-Cased**

    For Metric   1- **M_Single - Flush: 0762 x 2134 mm**
                       2 and 3- **M_Door -Interior-Single 4-Panel-Wood-0762 x 2134 mm**
                       4- **M_Door-Exterior-Single-Two_lite - 1200 x 2400 mm**
                       Door openings- **Passage Opening-Cased** resize to **2134 mm**

3. For Imperial   Window types to be used
                       1- **Fixed: 24" x 48"**
                       2- **Fixed: 48" x 48"** (with modified width)
    For Metric   Window types to be used
                       1- **Fixed: 0610 x 1220 mm**
                       2- **Fixed: 1220 x 1220 mm** (with modified width)

The following steps are required to complete this tutorial:

a. Open the file created in Chapter 3.
         For Imperial   *c03_Apartment1_tut3.rvt*
         For Metric   *M_c03_Apartment1_tut3.rvt*
    Invoke the **Door** tool.
b. Add doors at approximate locations, refer to Figures 4-3 through 4-8.
c. Load and add door openings, refer to Figure 4-9.
d. Place the door openings to the exact location based on the given parameters, refer to Figure 4-10 and Figure 4-11.
e. Invoke the **Window** tool. Select the window type by using the **Type Selector** drop-down list.
f. Place the windows at approximate locations.
g. Place the windows at the exact location as per the given dimensions, refer to Figures 4-12 through 4-16.
h. Save the project using the **Save As** tool.
         For Imperial   *c04_Apartment1_tut1.rvt*
         For Metric   *M_c04_Apartment1_tut1.rvt*
i. Close the project.

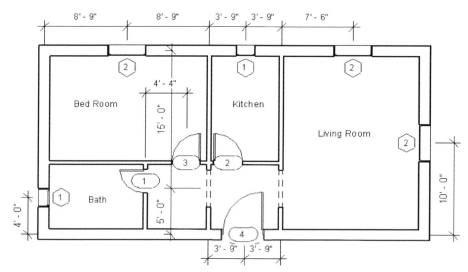

Figure 4-2 Sketch for adding doors and windows to the Apartment 1 project

Opening the Existing Project and Invoking the Door Tool

First, you need to open the specified project and invoke the **Door** tool from the **Architecture** tab.

1. Choose **Open > Project** from the **File** menu and open the *c03_Apartment1_tut3.rvt* for Imperial or *M_c03_Apartment1_tut3.rvt* for Metric project file created in Tutorial 3 of Chapter 3.

   You can also download this file from *http://www.cadsofttech.com*. The path of the file is as follows: *Textbooks > Civil/GIS > Revit Architecture > Revit Architecture 2019 For Novices*

2. Double-click on **Level 1** under the **Floor Plans** head in the **Project Browser**; the floor plan view is displayed.

3. Invoke the **Door** tool from the **Build** panel of the **Architecture** tab; the **Modify | Place Door** contextual tab is displayed.

4. On invoking the **Door** tool, the properties of the door to be added are displayed in the **Properties** palette. In the palette, select the type of door from the **Type Selector** drop-down list.

   For Imperial   **Single-Flush: 30" x 84"**
   For Metric   **M_Single - Flush: 0762 x 2134 mm**

5. Ensure that the **Tag on Placement** tool is chosen from the **Tag** panel of the **Modify | Place Door** contextual tab.

Adding Doors

In this section, you need to add doors at the approximate location and then modify its location by specifying the exact dimension. You will also use the **Load Family** tool to load the desired door type in the project.

1. Move the cursor close to the interior wall of the **Bath** area to display the door symbol, as shown in Figure 4-3. Notice that as you move the cursor, the side of the door is changed. Click on the interior wall; the door is created at the specified location.

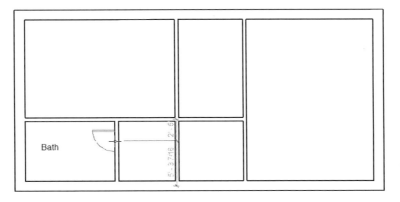

Figure 4-3 Specifying the location of the bath door

 Note
*You need to select the **Centerline** radio button in the **Temporary Dimension** dialog box for measuring center to center temporary dimensions.*

2. To move the door to the exact location, choose the **Modify** button in the **Select** panel of the **Modify | Doors** tab. Next, select the door added to the drawing; the selected door gets highlighted in blue with the controls and the related temporary dimensions displayed in it.

3. Since the location of the door is given with reference to the upper interior wall, click on the upper temporary dimension, and then enter **2'0"(610 mm)**, as shown in Figure 4-4. Next, press ENTER; the door moves to the specified location.

4. To place the door type 2, invoke the **Door** tool from the **Build** panel of the **Architecture** tab; the **Modify | Place Door** contextual tab is displayed.

5. Choose the **Load Family** tool in the **Mode** panel of this tab; the **Load Family** dialog box is displayed.

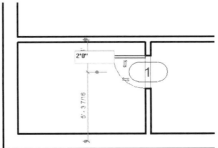

Figure 4-4 Moving the door to the exact location

6. In this dialog box, choose the **Doors > Residential** subfolder from the **US Imperial** folder.

Next, select the required door family.

For Imperial   **Door-Interior-Single-4-Panel-Wood**
For Metric   **M_Door-Interior-Single-4-Panel-Wood**

Next, choose the **Open** button; the **Specify Types** dialog box is displayed. In this dialog box, select the door type **36" x 84"(900 x 2100 mm)** from the **Types** area and choose the **OK** button.

7.   Next, ensure that the following door type is selected in the **Type Selector** drop-down list.
      For Imperial   **Door-Interior-Single-4-Panel-Wood 36" x 84"**
      For Metric   **M_Door-Interior-Single-4-Panel-Wood-900 x 2100 mm**

8.   Move the cursor near the interior wall common to the Lobby and the Kitchen areas, as shown in Figure 4-5, and click to add the kitchen door close to this location.

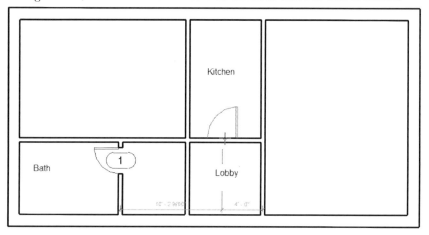

Figure 4-5 *Adding the door to the kitchen area*

9.   Choose the **Modify** button from the **Select** panel. Next, select the door inserted in the drawing; the door gets highlighted and its controls are displayed.

Notice that the door placed has the swing on the right side whereas the sketch shows a left side opening door, so you need to flip the swing side.

10. Click on the horizontal arrow key to flip the swing side. The swing side of the door is changed, as shown in Figure 4-6.

11. Click on the right side dimension to set it to **5'6"** (**1677 mm**), as shown in Figure 4-6.

12. Add the door of the same type in the bedroom area at a distance of **4'4"** (**1320 mm**) from the internal wall, as shown in Figure 4-7.

13. To create the entrance door of the apartment, choose the **Load Family** tool from the **Mode** panel of the **Modify | Place Door** tab; the **Load Family** dialog box is displayed. In this dialog box, add the **Door-Exterior-Single-Two Lite** for Imperial (**M_Door-Exterior-Single-Two Lite** for Metric) family type from the **Doors > Commercial** subfolder in the **US Imperial** folder.

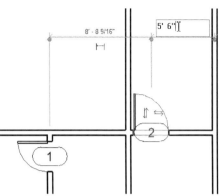

Figure 4-6 Using the flip control to change the swing side of the door

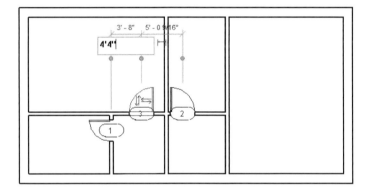

Figure 4-7 Specifying the location of the door in the bedroom area

14. Ensure that the **Door-Exterior-Single-Two_lite - 48" x 96"** option for Imperial or **M_Door-Exterior-Single-Two_lite - 1200 x 2400 mm** option for Metric is selected in the **Type Selector** drop-down list, and then add the door to the lobby area, as per the sketch plan, refer to Figure 4-8. While adding the door, you can use the spacebar to flip the door swing side.

15. After adding the door, choose the **Modify** button and select the recently created door; the temporary dimension is displayed. Click on the left of the temporary dimension and then enter the value **3'9"**(**1143 mm**), as shown in Figure 4-8, to move the door to the exact location as given in the sketch plan. Now, press ESC to exit the **Modify | Doors** tab.

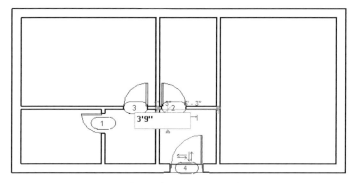

Figure 4-8 *Specifying the location of the entrance door*

Adding Door Openings

Next, you need to create two door openings in the lobby walls as given in the sketch plan. The openings can be loaded as door families but are added to the model as components.

1. Choose the **Insert** tab and then choose the **Load Family** tool from the **Load from Library** panel; the **Load Family** dialog box is displayed.

2. In the **Load Family** dialog box, select the **Passage Opening-Cased** family from the **Openings** sub-folder of the **US Imperial** folder or select the **M_Passage Opening-Cased** family from the **Openings** sub-folder of the **US Metric** folder. Next, choose the **Open** button to load this family; the **Passage Opening - Cased** family is added as a component type.

3. Invoke the **Place a Component** tool from **Architecture > Build > Component** drop-down; the **Modify | Place Component** tab is displayed.

4. Select the **Passage Opening - Cased 36" x 84"** option for Imperial or **M_Passage Opening - Cased 915 x 2134 mm** for Metric from the **Type Selector** drop-down list in the **Properties** palette, if it is not selected by default.

5. Move the cursor near the location shown in Figure 4-9 and then click to specify the location for the center of the opening. The opening is created.

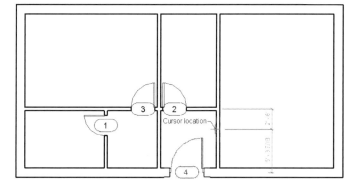

Figure 4-9 *Adding openings*

6. Now to modify the width of the opening, choose the **Modify** button from the **Select** panel. Select the recently created opening from the drawing; the **Modify | Generic Models** tab is displayed.

7. In this tab, choose the **Edit Type** tool from the **Properties** panel; the **Type Properties** dialog box is displayed.

8. Choose the **Duplicate** button; the **Name** dialog box is displayed. In this dialog box, enter **48" x 84"** for Imperial or **1220 x 2134 mm** for Metric in the **Name** edit box. Next, choose the **OK** button to close the **Name** dialog box.

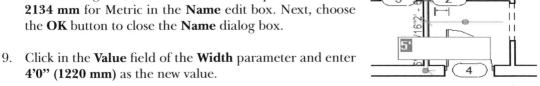

9. Click in the **Value** field of the **Width** parameter and enter **4'0" (1220 mm)** as the new value.

10. Choose the **OK** button in the **Type Properties** dialog box to close it.

Figure 4-10 Specifying the exact location of the opening

11. To move the opening to the exact location, click on lower temporary dimension, and enter **5'0"(1524 mm)**, as shown in Figure 4-10. Next, press ENTER and ESC to accept the value entered and exit the editing mode.

12. Similarly, create the opening of the same size and at the same distance on the opposite wall to complete the creation of doors and opening for the *Apartment 1* project. After adding them, the layout plan of the project will look similar to the plan shown in Figure 4-11.

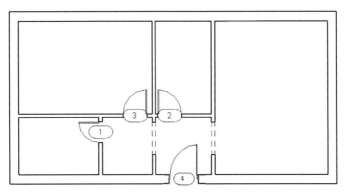

Figure 4-11 Layout plan with all doors and openings added

Tip
Doors and door openings can also be added to 3D view, sections, and elevations. You should, however, choose appropriate view to place the door. You can use the temporary dimensions to place the door at the exact location. In case you add a door incorrectly (for example, if the door is not entirely placed on the wall), Autodesk Revit displays a message, alerting you about the conflict and prompting you to take an appropriate action.

Adding Windows

The procedure of adding windows is quite similar to that of adding doors. Invoke the **Window** tool, select the window type, and add the window at an approximate location. You can then modify its location based on the sketch provided next in this tutorial.

1. Invoke the **Window** tool from the **Build** panel of the **Architecture** tab; the **Modify | Place Window** tab is displayed.

2. Ensure that the **Tag on Placement** tool is chosen from the **Tag** panel of the **Modify | Place Window** tab.

3. Click on the **Type Selector** drop-down list to view the in-built window types. To create the window number 1, select **Fixed 24" x 48"** for Imperial or **M_Fixed: 0610 x 1220 mm** for Metric from the drop-down list.

4. Move the cursor close to the exterior wall of the kitchen to display the window symbol, as shown in Figure 4-12. Add the window by clicking on the inner face of the exterior wall. The window is created at the specified location.

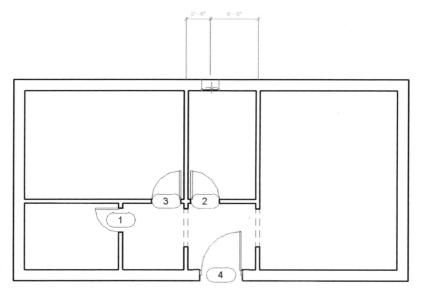

Figure 4-12 *Adding the kitchen window to the exterior wall*

5. To move the window to the exact location, choose the **Modify** button from the **Select** panel and then select the window from the drawing; it gets highlighted in blue and its controls are displayed.

6. Click on the left temporary dimension and enter **3'9"(1143 mm)**, as shown in Figure 4-13. Press ENTER; the window is moved to the specified location. Similarly, add another window of the same type near the external wall of the bath by invoking the **Window** tool from the **Build** panel.

7. After adding the window in the external wall of the bath, you need to move it to the exact location. To do so, select the window; it is highlighted in blue. Click on the lower temporary dimension; an edit box is displayed. Enter **4'0"(1220 mm)** in the edit box, refer to Figure 4-14, and then press ENTER. The window is moved to the desired location. Press the ESC key and exit.

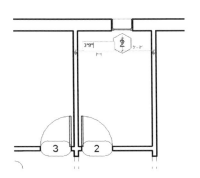

Figure 4-13 *Specifying the exact location of the window*

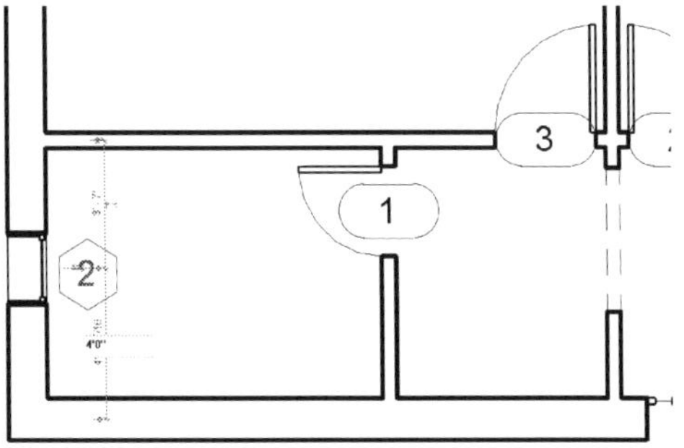

Figure 4-14 *Specifying the location of the bath window*

Now, you need to add the windows of type 2 to the drawing. These windows have a modified width of **4'0"(1220 mm)**. To add these windows, select the **Fixed: 24" x 48"** for Imperial or **M_Fixed: 0610 x 1220 mm** for Metric window type and create a window type duplicate. Modify window width to 4'0"(1220 mm) by using the **Type Properties** dialog box and add the window at the desired location.

8. Invoke the **Window** tool from the **Build** panel of the **Architecture** tab; the **Modify | Place Window** tab is displayed.

9. In the **Type Selector** drop-down list, select the **Fixed: 24" x 48"** (**M_Fixed: 610 x 1220 mm** for Metric) window type. Next, choose the **Edit Type** button in the **Properties** palette; the **Type Properties** dialog box is displayed.

10. In this dialog box, choose the **Duplicate** button; the **Name** dialog box is displayed. In the **Name** edit box, enter **48" x 48" (1220 x 1220 mm)** and then choose the **OK** button.

11. In the **Value** field for the **Width** type parameter, enter **4'0"(1220 mm)** and then choose the **Apply** and **OK** to close the **Type Properties** dialog box and return to the drawing window.

    Notice that the **Fixed: 48" x 48"** (**M_Fixed: 1220 x 1220 mm** for Metric) window type is added to the **Type Selector** drop-down list.

12. Move the cursor near the exterior wall of the bedroom and click to place the window. Press ESC twice to exit.

13. Now, select the added bedroom window; the window gets highlighted in blue color and its controls are displayed. Click on the temporary dimension displayed at the left and enter **8'9" (2667 mm)** to specify the location of the bedroom window, as shown in Figure 4-15.

The window moves at the desired location. Similarly, add the windows of the same type to the walls of the living room and specify their respective locations based on the sketch plan given, refer to Figures 4-16 and 4-17.

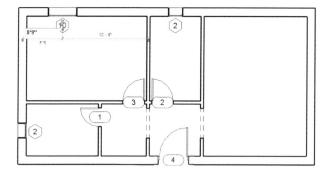

Figure 4-15 *Specifying the location of the bedroom window*

14. To change the window tag numbers, move the cursor over the number in any of the window tags marked 13 (tag number may vary) and double-click; an edit box is displayed. Enter **1** in the edit box and press ENTER; the **Revit** message box is displayed. Choose **Yes** in the message box; the window tag is renamed. Similarly, replace the other window tags marked 13 with the tag mark 1 and those marked 10 with the tag mark 2, refer to Figure 4-18. You will notice that the tag marks of other instances of the same window type are immediately modified.

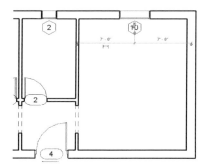 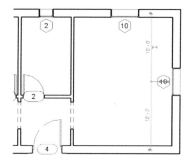

Figure 4-16 *Specifying the location of the first living room window*

Figure 4-17 *Adding the second living room window using temporary dimensions*

The Level 1 plan should look similar to the plan shown in Figure 4-18.

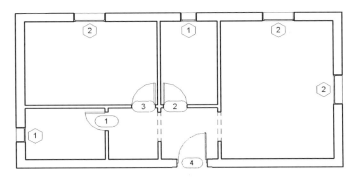

Figure 4-18 Completed project plan with renamed window tags

15. To view the plan in 3D, choose the **Default 3D View** tool from the **View > Create > 3D View** drop-down; the 3D view of the project is displayed, as shown in Figure 4-19.

Saving the Project

In this section, you will save the project file using the **Save As** tool.

1. Choose **Save As > Project** from **File** menu; the **Save As** dialog box is displayed. Create a folder with the name **c04_revit_2019_tut** and enter the desired name in the **File name** edit box.

    For Imperial   **c04_Apartment1_tut1**
    For Metric   **M_c04_Apartment1_tut1**
Choose **Save**; the file is saved.

2. Choose **Close** from **File** menu to close the project file.

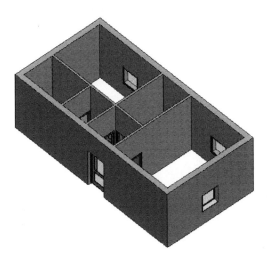

Figure 4-19 3D view of the Apartment 1 project

Tutorial 2   Club

In this tutorial, you will add doors and windows to Hall 1 and Lounge of the *Club* project created in Exercise 3 of Chapter 3. The centerline dimensions of the location of the doors and windows are given in Figure 4-20. You will create the doors and windows of Hall 2 in Exercise 2 later in this chapter. Use the following project file and parameters for this tutorial.

(Expected time: 30 min)

1. Project file-
        For Imperial   *c03_Club_ex3.rvt*
        For Metric   *M_c03_Club_ex3.rvt*

2. Door types to be used
        For Imperial   1, 2, and 3- **Door-Interior-Single-Full Glass Wood- 36" x 84"**
                                 4- **Door-Single-Panel: 36" x 84"**
                                 5- **Door- Double- Glass - 72"x 84"**
        For Metric   1, 2, and 3-
                                 M_Door-Interior-Single-Full Glass Wood- 900 x 2100 mm
                                 4- **M_Door- Single- Panel: 900 x 2100 mm**
                                 5- **M_Door- Double- Glass - 1800 x 2050 mm**

3. Window types to be used
        For Imperial   1- **Fixed: 36" x 48"**
        For Metric   1- **M_Fixed: 0915 x 1220 mm**

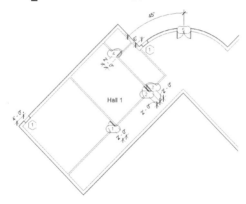

Figure 4-20   *Sketch plan for adding doors and windows to the Club project*

The following steps are required to complete this tutorial:

a. Open the file created in Chapter 3.
        For Imperial   *c03_Club_ex3.rvt*
        For Metric   *M_c03_Club_ex3.rvt*
      Invoke the **Door** tool.
b. Select the door type by using the **Type Selector** drop-down list.
c. Add the doors at approximate locations, refer to Figures 4-21 through 4-28.
d. Change the placement of the door to the desired location.
e. Invoke the **Window** tool and select the window type using the **Type Selector** drop-down list.

f.   Add the windows at approximate locations, refer to Figures 4-29 through 4-31.

g.   Modify the placement of windows to the exact location, based on the given sketch plan.

h.   Save the project using the **Save As** tool.

       For Imperial   *c04_Club_tut2.rvt*

       For Metric   **M**_*c04_Club_tut2.rvt*

i.   Close the project.

Opening the Existing Project and Invoking the Door Tool

First, you need to open the *Club* project and then invoke the **Door** tool.

1.   Choose **Open > Project** from the **File** menu and open the *c03_Club_ex3.rvt* for Imperial *M_c03_Club_ex3.rvt* for Metric project file created in Exercise 3 of Chapter 3. You can also download this file from *http://www.cadsofttech.com*. The path of the file is as follows: *Textbooks > Civil/GIS > Revit Architecture > Revit Architecture 2019 For Novices*

2.   Invoke the **Door** tool from the **Build** panel of the **Architecture** tab; the **Modify | Place Door** tab is displayed. Alternatively, type **DR**.

Selecting a Door Type

Select the door type 1 and add it to the project. The project parameters indicate that the door type is to be loaded from the **US Imperial** folder. To access the **US Imperial** folder, choose the **Load Family** tool from the **Mode** panel of the **Modify | Place Door** tab.

1.   Choose the **Load Family** tool from the **Mode** panel in the **Modify | Place Door** tab; the **Load Family** dialog box is displayed.

2.   In this dialog box, open the **Doors > Residential** folder and select the door type **Door-Interior-Single-Full Glass Wood**. Choose **Open** to load the family of this door type; the **Specify Types** dialog box is displayed. Select the **36" x 84"** from the **Types** area and choose the **OK** button.

3.   Next, ensure that the **Door-Interior-Single-Full Glass Wood: 36" x 84"** option for Imperial or **M_Door-Interior-Single-Full Glass Wood- 900 x 2100 mm** option for Metric is selected by default in the **Type Selector** drop-down list.

Adding Doors

You can add a door at the desired location by clicking at an approximate point in its host wall and then modifying its location by specifying the exact dimension. First you need to add the door type 1 and then the other door types.

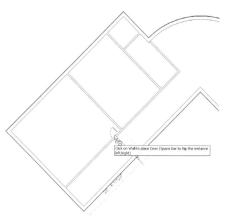

1. Move the cursor close to the interior wall face to display the door symbol, as shown in Figure 4-21. Notice that the side of the door changes as you move the cursor.

2. Place the door by clicking on the interior wall and then press ESC twice to exit. On doing so, the door is added to the location.

Figure 4-21 Adding the door

3. To move the door to the exact location, select the door; it gets highlighted in blue and its controls are displayed.

4. As the location of the door is given with reference to the interior wall, click on the right temporary dimension and enter **2'0"(610 mm)**, as shown in Figure 4-22. Press ESC to exit the setting of dimensions. The door moves to the desired location.

Note

Depending on the placement of the cursor, the door side and swing might not be same as desired. If required, click on the flip control arrows or the door swing arrows to achieve the desired orientation.

5. Add the next door using the same door type by clicking at the approximate location, as shown in Figure 4-23. Press ESC twice.

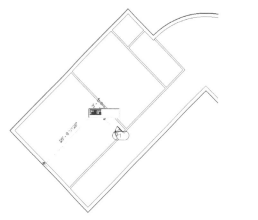
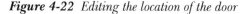
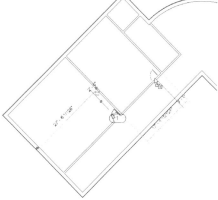

Figure 4-22 Editing the location of the door   *Figure 4-23 Adding next door*

6. Now, select the door and click on the temporary dimension between the door center and the interior wall and enter the value **3'0"(914.4 mm)** in the edit box, as shown in Figure 4-24. The door moves to the desired location.

7. Add another door at the location shown in Figure 4-25. You may need to use the flip arrows to orient the door swing in the desired direction.

8. Load the door and select **Door-Single-Panel -36" x 84"** option for Imperial or **M_Door-Interior-Single-1_Panel-900 x 2100mm** option for Metric from the **Type Selector** drop-down list, as specified in the project parameters.

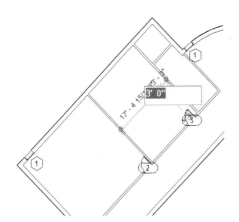

Figure 4-24 *Editing the location of the next door*

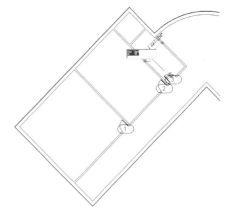

Figure 4-25 *Specifying the location of the next door*

9. Move the cursor near the interior wall and click to add the door close to the location, as shown in Figure 4-26. Press ESC to exit.

10. Select the door added last in the drawing; it gets highlighted in blue and its controls are displayed.

11. Click on the right side dimension and enter **3'0"(914.4 mm)**, as shown in Figure 4-26.

12. To create the entrance door, invoke the **Door** tool again and then choose the **Load Family** tool from the **Mode** panel; the **Load Family** dialog box is displayed. In the dialog box, load **Door- Double-Glass** from the **US Imperial > Doors** folder; the **Specify Types** dialog box is displayed. Select the **72" x 84"** in the **Types** area and choose the **OK** button.

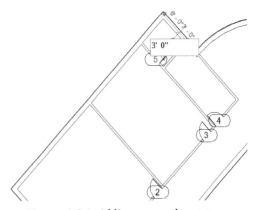

Figure 4-26 *Adding a new door type*

13. Ensure that the **Door- Double-Glass: 72" x 84"** door type is selected for Imperial or **M_Door-Double-Glass -1800 x 2050 mm** for Metric from the **Type Selector** drop-down list in the **Properties** palette, if not selected by default.

14. Move the cursor near the main door location, as shown in Figure 4-27. Press SPACEBAR to flip the swing side of the door to the desired side, if required, and click to create the door.

15. Click on the temporary dimension and set the angle to 46 degrees, as shown in Figure 4-28. Press ENTER.

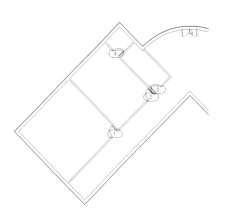   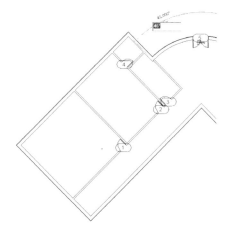

Figure 4-27 Adding the entrance door   *Figure 4-28 Specifying the angular dimension*

16. Press ESC twice to exit the selection.

Adding Windows

The procedure for adding windows is similar to that for adding doors. After invoking the **Window** tool and selecting the required window type, click at the approximate location to add it. The location can then be modified to the exact dimension as specified in the sketch plan.

1. Choose **Window** from the **Build** panel of the **Architecture** tab; the **Modify | Place Window** tab is displayed.

2. Select the **Fixed 36" x 48"** option for Imperial **M_Fixed: 0915 x 1220mm** for Metric from the **Type Selector** drop-down list in the **Properties** palette.

3. Move the cursor close to the exterior wall of Hall 1 to display the window symbol, as shown in Figure 4-29. Add the window by clicking on the exterior wall.

Tip
*If tags are not displayed with doors and windows then choose the **Tag on Placement** tool from the **Tag** panel of the **Modify | Place Window** tab.*

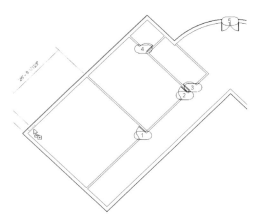

Figure 4-29 *Moving the cursor near the wall of Hall 1 to add window*

4. Next, to move the window to the exact location, choose the **Modify** button from the **Select** panel. Then, select the window, click on the lower temporary dimension, and enter **4'0"(1219 mm)**, as shown in Figure 4-30. The window moves to the desired location.

5. Repeat step 1 through step 3 to add another window by clicking near the left end of the curved wall, refer to Figure 4-31.

6. Select the window created and enter **6** as the angular dimension, as shown in Figure 4-31. The window moves to the desired location.

7. Next, select the window tag and click on the tag number; an edit box is displayed. Enter **1** in the edit box and press ENTER; the **Revit** message box is displayed. Choose **Yes**; the window tag is renamed.

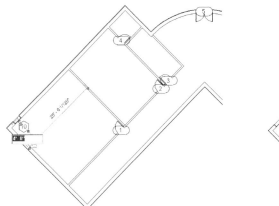

Figure 4-30 *Editing the location of the window*

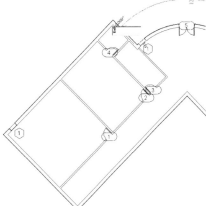

Figure 4-31 *Adding windows*

Saving the Project

In this section, you will save the project file using the **Save As** tool.

1. Choose **Save As > Project** from the **File** menu and enter the required name in the **File name** edit box of the **Save As** dialog box.

    For Imperial   **c04_Club_tut2**
    For Metric   **M_c04_Club_tut2**

    Choose the save button. The project file is saved.

2. Choose **Close** from the **File** menu to close the project file.

EXERCISES

Exercise 1   Apartment 2

Add doors, windows, and openings to the *Apartment 2* project, created in Exercise 1 of Chapter 3, refer to Figure 4-32. The dimensions and text need not to be mentioned. Use the following project parameters: **(Expected time: 30 min)**

1. Project file-

    For Imperial   *c03_Apartment2_ex1.rvt*
    For Metric   *M_c03_Apartment2_ex1.rvt*

2. Door types to be used:

    For Imperial   Bath and kitchen doors- **Door- Single - Panel: 36" x 84"**
                      Bedroom and Lobby door- **Door-Interior-Double-Full Glass Wood - 36" x 84"**
                      Door openings in dining (dashed lines)- **4'0" x 7'0"** using **Passage-Opening Cased : 36"x 84"**
                      Distance of the door centerlines from wall centerlines- **2'0"**
    For Metric   Bath and kitchen doors- **M_Door- Single- Panel: 0915 x 2134 mm**
                      Bedroom door- **M_Door-Interior-Double-Full Glass Wood- 1500 x 2000 mm**
                      Lobby door- **M_Double-Interior-Double-Full Glass Wood - 900 x 2100 mm**
                      Door openings in dining (dashed lines)- **1220 x 2134 mm** using **M_Passage-Opening Cased : 0915 x 2134 mm**
                      Distance of the door centerlines from wall centerlines- **610 mm**

3. Window types to be used

    For Imperial   Bedroom and living room windows - **Fixed: 36" x 48"**
                      Bath and kitchen windows- **Fixed: 24" X 48"**
    For Metric   Bedroom and living room windows - **M_Fixed: 0915 x 1220 mm**
                      Bath and kitchen windows- **M_Fixed: 0610 X 1220 mm**

4. File name to be saved-

    For Imperial   **c04_Apartment2_ex1**
    For Metric   **M_c04_Apartment2_ex1**

    For the distance of window centerlines from wall centerlines refer to Figure 4-32.

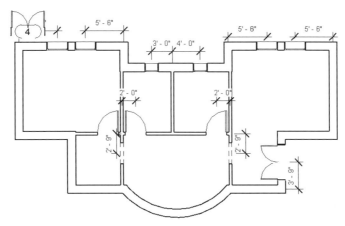

Figure 4-32 *Sketch plan for adding doors and windows to the Apartment 2 project*

Exercise 2   Elevator and Stair Lobby

Add doors, windows, and openings to the *Elevator and Stair Lobby* project created in Exercise 2 of Chapter 3, refer to Figure 4-33. Do not add text or dimensions as they are given for reference only. Use the following project parameters.   **(Expected time: 30 min)**

1. Project File-
    For Imperial   *c03_ElevatorandStairLobby_ex2.rvt*
    For Metric   *M_c03_ElevatorandStairLobby_ex2.rvt*

2. Door types to be used-
    For Imperial   **Single - Flush: 36" x 84"**,
                       Distance of door centerlines from wall centerlines- **2'6"**
                       Door openings - **4'0" x 7'0"**
                       Passage Opening-Cased- 36" x 84"
    For Metric   **M_Single - Flush: 0915 x 2134 mm**
                       Distance of door centerlines from wall centerlines- **762 mm**
                       Door openings - **1220 x 2134 mm**
                       Passage Opening-Cased- 0915 x 2134 mm

3. Window types to be used:
    For Imperial   **Fixed: 36" x 48"**
    For Metric   **M_Fixed: 0915 x 1220 mm**

4. File name to be saved-
    For Imperial   **c04_ElevatorandStairLobby_ex2**
    For Metric   **M_c04_ElevatorandStairLobby_ex2**

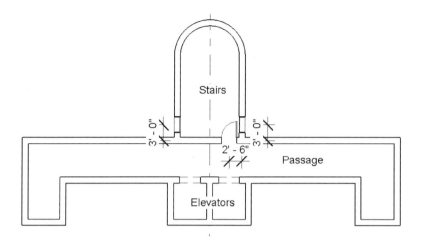

Figure 4-33 *Sketch plan for adding doors, windows, and openings to the Elevator and Stair Lobby project*

For Imperial	W1- **Fixed: 24" x 24"**
	W2- **Fixed: 36" x 72"**
For Metric	W1- **M_Fixed: 0600 x 0600 mm**
	W2- **M_Fixed: 0900 x 1800 mm**

4.   File name to be saved-

        For Imperial   **c04_residential_door_window_ex4**

        For Metric   **M_c04_residential_door_window_ex4**

Chapter 5

Using the Editing Tools

Learning Objectives

After completing this chapter, you will be able to:
- *Create a selection set of elements*
- *Move and copy elements*
- *Use the Trim and Extend tools*
- *Use the Cut and Paste tools*
- *Use the Rotate, Mirror, and Offset tools*
- *Create an array of elements using the Array tool*
- *Use the Match, Align, Delete, Lock, and Group tools*

CREATING A SELECTION SET

In order to edit an element or a group of elements, you must first select them. To create a selection set, first you need to exit the currently invoked tool. To do so, choose the **Modify** button from the **Select** panel of the contextual tab or type **MD** to exit the current tool. After exiting the current tool, move the cursor near the element that you wish to select. On doing so, you will notice that it gets highlighted and its description is displayed in the **Status Bar**. In case, there are elements in proximity of the element to be selected, press the TAB key to cycle between them. Click to select the element when it is highlighted. By default a selected element will appear semi-transparent and blue in color. In the forthcoming sections, you will learn different methods of selecting multiple elements, restoring the selected elements, and removing elements from a selection.

Selecting Multiple Elements

The methods of selecting multiple elements are discussed next.

Using the CTRL Key
Using the Selection Window
Using the TAB Key (For Walls)
Using the Select All Instances Option
Isolating Elements Using the Selection Box

Selecting Elements Using the Advanced Tools

In Autodesk Revit, besides the basic selection tools, you can use the advanced selection tools for selection and modification purpose. These advanced tools are available in the **Status Bar**, as shown in Figure 5-1. These tools are discussed next.

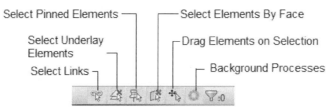

Figure 5-1 *The tools in the* ***Status Bar***

MODIFYING TOOLS

In Revit, there are various tools that can be used to edit the sketched entities. These tools are used to trim, move, copy extend, offset, or mirror the sketched entities. You can also perform various other editing operations by using these tools. Various editing operations and the tools used to perform them are:

Move and copy elements
Trim and Extend elements
Cut and paste elements
Rotate elements
Mirroring elements
Offset Elements
Array elements
Matching Elements

Aligning elements and working with constraints
Deleting elements
Splitting elements
Group Elements
Pinning and unpinning elements
Scaling elements
Measuring Distance Between References and Along an Element

TUTORIALS

Tutorial 1 Apartment 1

In this tutorial, you will modify the *c04_Apartment1_tut1.rvt* project file created in Tutorial 1 of Chapter 4. You will copy, move, and mirror the windows to create the project, refer to Figure 5-2. Do not add the dimensions and text as they are given only for reference. Use the following project parameters: **(Expected time: 30 min)**
The following steps are required to complete this tutorial:

a. Open the required file created in Chapter 4.
　　For Imperial　　*c04_Apartment1_tut1.rvt*
　　For Metric　　　*M_c04_Apartment1_tut1.rvt*
b. Create the window type W5 using the **Window** tool, refer to Figure 5-3.
c. Use the **Copy** tool to create the windows at the desired locations, refer to Figures 5-4 and 5-5.
d. Use the **Group** tool to group the twin windows W3, refer to Figures 5-6 and 5-7.
e. Use the **Mirror** tool to mirror windows, refer to Figures 5-7 and 5-8.
f. Save the project using the **Save As** tool.
　　For Imperial　　*c05_Apartment1_tut1.rvt*
　　For Metric　　　*M_c05_Apartment1_tut1.rvt*
g. Close the project.

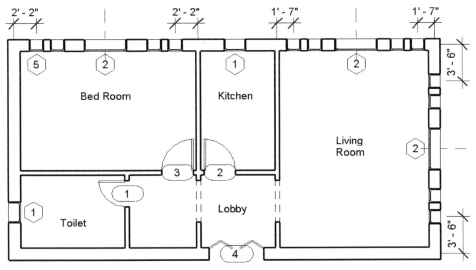

Figure 5-2 Sketch plan of the Apartment1 project

Opening the Project and Creating the Window

You need to open the specified project and add the left side bedroom window using the **Window** tool (see Adding Windows section in Chapter 4).

1. Choose **Open > Project** from the **File** menu and open the file created in Tutorial 1 of Chapter 4.

    For Imperial   *c04_Apartment1_tut1.rvt*
    For Metric   *M_c04_Apartment1_tut1.rvt*

    You can also download this file from *http://www.cadsofttech.com*. The path of the file is as follows: *Textbooks > Civil/GIS > Revit Architecture > Revit Architecture 2019 For Novices*

2. In the Project Browser, double-click on **Level 1** under the **Floor Plans** head.

3. Invoke the **Window** tool from the **Build** panel of the **Architecture** tab. Next, in the **Properties** palette, select the required option from the **Type Selector** drop-down list.

    For Imperial   **Fixed 16"x48"**
    For Metric   **Fixed 406 x 1220mm**

4. Click near the top exterior wall of the bed room to create a window and then modify the temporary dimensions, as shown in Figure 5-3. Press ESC twice to exit the **Window** tool.

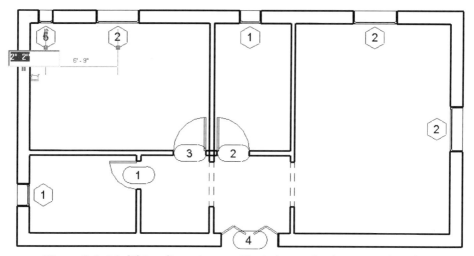

Figure 5-3 *Modifying dimension to add window to the Apartment 1 project*

Creating a Copy of the Window

Next, you need to copy the window type created in the previous section and then create another window at the specified distance.

1. Select the recently created window from the drawing area by clicking on it. On doing so, the **Modify | Windows** tab is displayed.

2. Invoke the **Copy** tool from the **Modify** panel; the window enclosed in the preview box is displayed indicating that it has been selected for copying. Ensure that the **Constrain** check box is selected in the **Options Bar**.

3. Move the cursor near the midpoint of the window you just created and click to specify the first point of the copy distance when the mid-point snap is displayed, as shown in Figure 5-4.

4. Move the cursor toward the right and type **2'0"(610 mm)** in the edit box displayed. Next, press ENTER; the window is copied at the specified distance, as shown in Figure 5-5. Now, press ESC to exit the **Modify | Windows** tab.

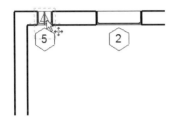 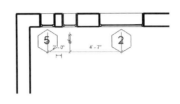

Figure 5-4 *Specifying the first point of the copy distance*

Figure 5-5 *Specifying the distance at which the copy of the window will be placed*

Grouping Windows

In this section, you will create a group using the **Create Group** tool. Since these windows appear at the same distance at all occurrences in the project, you can group them as a single entity and then create the copies. Use the pick box option for selecting the windows and then use the **Create Group** tool to group them.

1. Using the pick box selection method, select the two windows; the two windows are highlighted, refer to Figure 5-6

2. Invoke the **Create Group** tool from the **Create** panel of the **Modify | Windows** tab; the **Create Model Group and Attached Detail Group** dialog box is displayed.

3. Specify **2XW3** as the name of the group in the **Name** edit box and choose the **OK** button.

    The windows are grouped and a preview box is displayed. Also, the group origin controls are displayed, as shown in Figure 5-7.

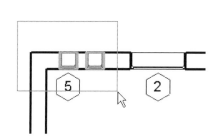

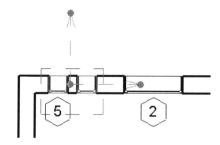

Figure 5-6 *Selecting the windows by*   ***Figure 5-7*** *Grouped windows with the*
using the pick box selection method   *group origin controls displayed*

Mirroring and Copying Windows

Now, the twin windows need to be mirrored and copied using the **Mirror - Pick Axis** tool.
The sketch plan shows that the twin windows of the bedroom are equidistant from the center
of the window tagged 2(W2). You will use this point to create a mirror axis to mirror the
windows.

1. Invoke the **Mirror - Pick Axis** tool from the **Modify** panel in the **Modify | Model Groups**
    tab.
    The mirror tools are available because the created group is already selected and highlighted.

2. Move the cursor near the midpoint of the window tagged 2 (W2) until a vertical line is
    displayed, as shown in Figure 5-8. This line indicates the midpoint and the mirror axis. Click
    at this location; the windows are mirrored on the other side of the mirror axis, as shown in
    Figure 5-9.

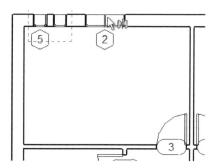

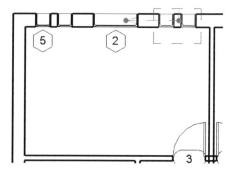

Figure 5-8 *Specifying the mirror axis to mirror*   ***Figure 5-9*** *Windows created after mirroring*
the twin windows

Placing Grouped Windows

Next, you need to place the grouped windows on the exterior wall of the living room by
dragging and dropping the group in the drawing.

1. In the **Project Browser**, click on the '+' sign in the **Groups** node of the **Project Browser**
    to display the created groups. Click on the '+' sign corresponding to the **Model** sub-node;
    it displays **2XW3** as the group in the project.

2.	To place this group in the project, click on the group name in the **Project Browser** and drag and drop it on the exterior wall of the living room, as shown in Figure 5-10. Click to place the group.

3.	Select the placed group, as shown in Figure 5-11, and choose the **Activate** | Activate Dimensions | **Dimensions** button from the **Options Bar**. Click on the left dimension and enter **1'7"(483 mm)**; the group moves to the desired location.

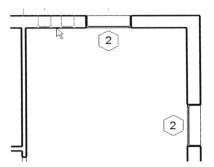

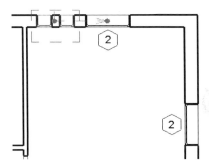

Figure 5-10 *Dragging and dropping a group from the **Project Browser***

Figure 5-11 *Selecting the group to move to the desired location*

4.	Create a mirror image of the twin windows using the midpoint of the central window as the mirror axis. The windows are mirrored, as shown in Figure 5-12.

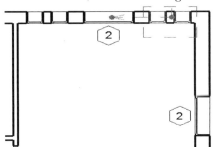

Figure 5-12 *Mirrored windows*

5.	Repeat steps 1, 2, and 3 to place the window group on the upper side of the right exterior wall of the living room. Use the same distance parameter as specified in the sketch plan, refer to Figure 5-2. After placing the window group, create a mirror image of the group using the midpoint of the central window. Use the dimensions shown in Figure 5-2 to specify the exact location of the group. Press ESC to exit the **Modify | Model Groups** tab.

Saving the Project

In this section, you will save the project file using the **Save As** tool.

1.	Choose **Save As > Project** from the **File** menu; the **Save As** dialog box is displayed. Browse to the folder **c05_revit_2019_tut** and choose the **Open** button; the **File Name** edit box is displayed.

Enter the required file name in the **File name** edit box.

For Imperial	**c05_Apartment1_tut1**
For Metric	**M_c05_Apartment1_tut1**

Choose the **Save** button; the file gets saved and the **Save As** dialog box is closed.

2. Choose **Close** from the **File** menu to close the project file.

The completed project will look similar to the one shown in Figure 5-13.

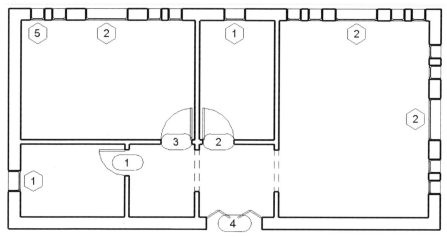

Figure 5-13 *The completed Apartment 1 project*

Tutorial 2   Club

In this tutorial, you will modify Hall 1 and Lounge of the *Club* project created in Tutorial 2 of Chapter 4. You will move and copy the windows to their desired locations and modify their size and type, refer to Figure 5-14. Do not create the dimensions and text as they are only for reference. Use the following project parameters: **(Expected time: 30 min)**

1. Project File-

For Imperial	*c04_Club_tut2.rvt*
For Metric	*M_c04_Club_tut2.rvt*

2. Window types to be used:

For Imperial	W1- **Fixed 36"x48"**
For Metric	W1- **Fixed 0915 x 1220 mm**

The following steps are required to complete this tutorial:

a. Open the required file created in Chapter 4.

For Imperial	*c04_Club_tut2.rvt*
For Metric	*M_c04_Club_tut2.rvt*

b. Create an array of four windows of Hall 1 by selecting the **Linear** option of the **Array** tool, refer to Figures 5-15 and 5-16.

c. Create an array of windows of the Lounge by selecting the **Radial** option of the **Array** tool, refer to Figures 5-17 to 5-20.

d.   Use the **Create Group** tool to group the four windows W1 as a single entity.
e.   Use the **Mirror - Pick Axis** and **Mirror - Draw Axis** tools to mirror the grouped windows, refer to Figures 5-20 to 5-23.
f.   Use the **Copy** tool to copy the grouped windows, refer to Figures 5-24 and 5-25.
g.   Save the project using the **Save As** tool.
    For Imperial   *c05_Club_tut2.rvt*
    For Metric   *M_c05_Club_tut2.rvt*
h.   Close the project.

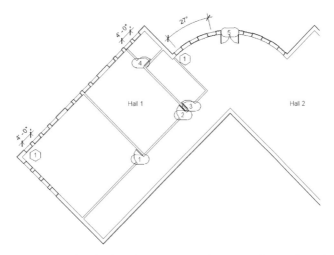

Figure 5-14 *Sketch plan for moving and copying the windows in the Club project*

Opening an Existing Project and Creating an Array of Windows

In Figure 5-14, notice that the windows of Hall 1 appear in three clusters of four windows each in the sketch plan. The four windows are equidistant, 4'0"(1220 mm) apart. You can create them using the **Linear** option of the **Array** tool. Similarly, to create the four windows of the Lounge, use the **Radial** option.

1.   Choose **Open > Project** from the **File** menu and open the desired file.
    For Imperial   *c04_Club_tut2.rvt*
    For Metric   *M_c04_Club_tut2.rvt*

You can also download this file from *http://www.cadsofttech.com*. The path of the file is as follows: *Textbooks > Civil/GIS > Revit Achitecture> Revit Architecture 2019 For Novices*

2.   Move the cursor on the lower left window tagged 1(W1) of Hall 1 and click to select the window.

3.   Invoke the **Array** tool from the **Modify** panel of the **Modify | Windows** tab; the window is enclosed in a dashed rectangular box indicating that it has been selected for creating an array.

4. In the **Options Bar**, ensure that the **Linear** button is chosen and the **2nd** radio button is selected in the **Move To** area. Also, ensure that the **Constrain** check box is cleared.

5. In the **Number** edit box of the **Options Bar**, enter **4**.

6. Now, move the cursor near the midpoint of the selected window and click when the midpoint object snap is displayed, as shown in Figure 5-15; the start point of the linear array is specified. Ensure that the **Group and Associate** check box is selected.

7. Move the cursor upward along the wall incline and enter the value **4'0"(1220 mm)**, as shown in Figure 5-16; a text box with the number of array elements is displayed.

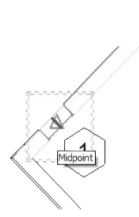

Figure 5-15 *Specifying the first point of the array distance*

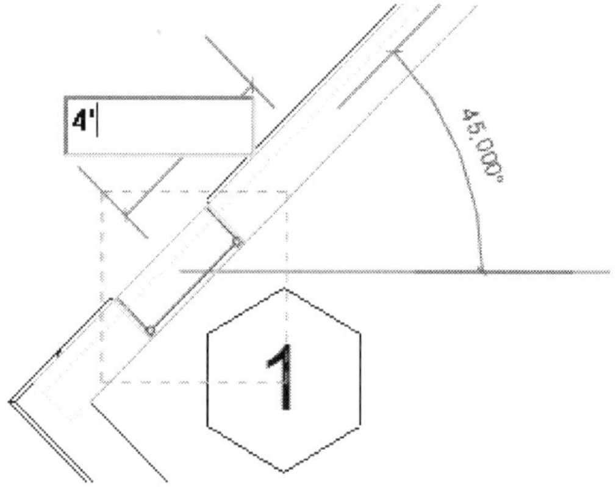

Figure 5-16 *Entering the value of the array distance*

8. Press ENTER to accept the value; an array is created. Notice that as you move the cursor, a preview box showing the location of the selected elements is displayed.

    Similarly, the windows of the Lounge can be created using the **Radial** option of the **Array**.

9. Move the cursor over the exterior window at the Lounge area tagged 1(W1), and click when it is highlighted; the window is selected.

10. Next, invoke the **Array** tool from the **Modify** panel of the **Modify | Windows** tab.

11. In the **Options Bar**, choose the **Radial** button. Also, ensure the **Group and Associate** check box is selected.

12. Select the **Last** radio button in the **Move To** area of the **Options Bar**. To create three windows, enter the value **3** in the **Number** edit box, if it is not entered by default.

    As the center of the required radial array is the center of the circular wall, you need to move the rotation point to it and then create the radial array.

13. In the **Options Bar**, choose the **Place** button and place the cursor at the center of the curved wall, as shown in Figure 5-17. Alternatively, you can move the cursor near the rotation key of the selected window and drag it to the center of the curved wall.

    Notice that the radial array line now originates from the new center point.

14. Move the cursor near the midpoint of the Lounge window and click when the **Midpoint** object snap is displayed, as shown in Figure 5-18; the start point of the radial array is specified.

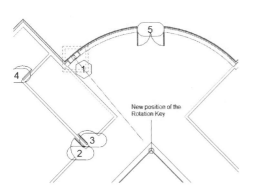

Figure 5-17 *Rotation key moved to the new rotation point*

Figure 5-18 *Specifying the first point of the array*

15. Move the cursor clockwise along the curved wall and enter **27** as the temporary angular dimension, as given in the sketch plan and shown in Figure 5-19.

16. Next, press ENTER twice to accept the value specified for the angular dimension and the number of array elements; the radial array is created, as shown in Figure 5-20.

17. Choose the **Modify** button from the **Select** panel to exit the current selection.

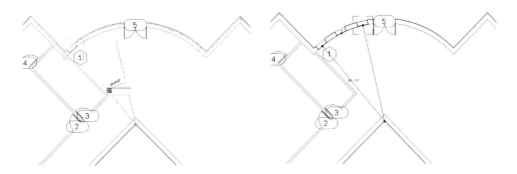

Figure 5-19 *Specifying the array angle*

Figure 5-20 *Radial array of the selected window*

Grouping the Cluster of Windows

The sketch plan shows the cluster of four Hall 1 windows appearing together. Group them for the ease of copying. You can use the **Create Group** tool to group the array of windows.

1. Move the cursor near the four windows of the Hall 1 and select them using the CTRL key.

2. Invoke the **Create Group** tool from the **Create** panel of the **Modify | Model Groups** tab; the **Create Model Group** dialog box is displayed. The default name of the group of windows in the dialog box is Group 1.

3. Specify **4XW1- Linear Windows** as the group name in the **Name** edit box.

4. Choose the **OK** button in the dialog box; the windows are grouped and the group name is displayed in the **Groups** node of the **Project Browser** in the **Model** subhead.

Mirroring the Grouped Windows

You need to mirror the grouped windows of Hall 1 and the radial windows of the Lounge using the **Mirror - Pick Axis** and **Mirror - Draw Axis** tools.

1. Move the cursor near the grouped windows of Hall 1 and click; the grouped windows are selected and highlighted, as shown in Figure 5-21.

2. Choose the **Mirror - Pick Axis** tool from the **Modify** panel of the **Modify | Model Groups** tab. Also, ensure that the **Copy** check box is selected in the **Options Bar**.

3. Move the cursor near the interior wall and click when the cursor snaps to the wall centerline; the wall centerline is selected as the mirror axis, as shown in Figure 5-22, and the grouped windows are mirrored to the other end of the exterior wall. Ignore the warning message that is displayed due to the conflicts between the interior wall and the window. Now, choose the **Modify** button from the **Select** panel or press ESC to exit the current selection.

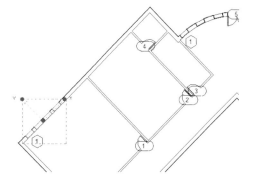
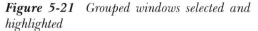
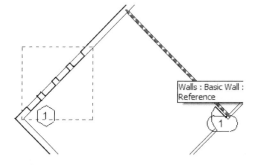

Figure 5-21 *Grouped windows selected and highlighted*

Figure 5-22 *Using the wall centerline as the mirror axis*

Notice that the same window type is also placed on the lower left perpendicular wall. You can use the **Mirror - Draw Axis** tool to mirror the grouped windows to the perpendicular wall.

4.   Click on the original grouped windows to select them.

5.   Invoke the **Mirror - Draw Axis** tool from the **Modify | Model Groups** tab.

6.   In the **Options Bar**, ensure that the **Copy** check box is selected.

7.   Move the cursor to the intersection of the two perpendicular walls and click when the endpoint object snap is displayed; the first point of the mirror line is specified.

8.   Move the cursor horizontally and click when the dashed line is displayed, as shown in Figure 5-23; the second point of the mirror axis is specified. Now, choose the **Modify** button from the **Select** panel to exit the current selection.

9.   The grouped windows are mirrored to the perpendicular wall, as shown in Figure 5-24.

     Similarly, mirror the three radial windows of the Lounge to the other side of the door using the **Mirror - Draw Axis** tool. Draw the vertical axis from the center of the curved wall as the mirror axis.

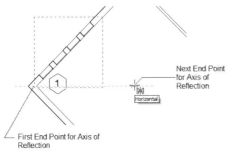

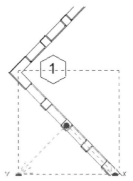

Figure 5-23 *Using the horizontal axis as the mirror reference line*

Figure 5-24 *Mirrored windows on the perpendicular wall*

Copying the Grouped Windows
You can use the **Copy** tool to copy the grouped windows of Hall 1.

1.   Select the original grouped window of Hall 1.

2.   Invoke the **Copy** tool from the **Modify | Model Groups** tab.

3.   Select the group origin or the midpoint of the grouped windows as the start point of the copy distance.

4. Move the cursor upward along the external wall and choose the endpoint of the central internal wall as the second point of the copy distance, as shown in Figure 5-25. On doing so, the grouped window is copied at the desired location, as shown in Figure 5-26. Ignore the warning message, if any, displayed.

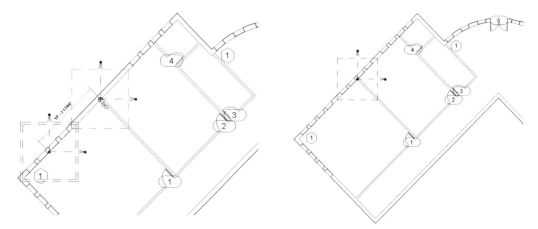

Figure 5-25 *Specifying the start and end points of the copy distance*   ***Figure 5-26*** *Grouped windows copied*

Saving the Project

In this section, you will save the project file using the **Save As** tool.

1. Choose **Save As > Project** from the **File** menu; the **Save As** dialog box is displayed. Browse to the folder **c05_revit_2019_tut** and choose the **Open** button; the **File name** edit box is displayed.

.

    Enter the required file in the **File name** edit box
        For Imperial   **c05_Club_tut2**
        For Metric   **M_c05_Club_tut2**
    Choose **Save**; the file is saved and the dialog box gets closed.

2. Choose **Close** from the **File** menu to close the project file.

EXERCISES

Exercise 1   Apartment 2

Add windows to the exterior wall of the dining area of the *Apartment 2* project created in Exercise 1 of Chapter 4 based on Figure 5-27. The dimensions and text are given only for reference and are not to be added. The parameters to be used for the project are given next.

(Expected time: 30 min)

1. Project-
        For Imperial   *c04_Apartment2_ex1.rvt*
        For Metric   *M_c04_Apartment2_ex1.rvt*

2. Window type to be added in the dining area-
     For Imperial   **Fixed: 24"X48"**
     For Metric   **Fixed: 0610 x 1220 mm**
3. Name of the file to be saved-
     For Imperial   **c05_Apartment2_ex1**
     For Metric   **M_c05_Apartment2_ex1**

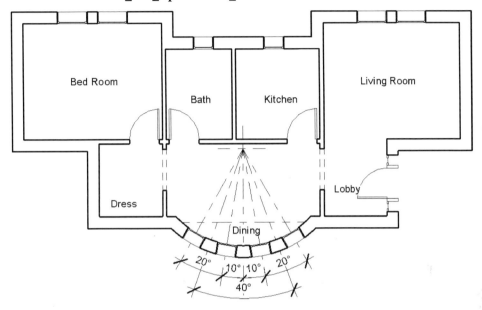

Figure 5-27 *Sketch plan for adding windows to the Apartment 2 project*

Exercise 2   **Club**

Add windows, as shown in Figure 5-28, to the Hall 2 of the *Club* project created in Tutorial 2 of this chapter. The dimensions and text have been given for reference and need not to be added.

                                               (Expected time: 30 min)

1. Project File-
     For Imperial   *c04_Club_ex3*
     For Metric   *M_ c04_Club_ex3*
2. Window types to be used -
     For Imperial   W1- **Fixed: 36" X 48"**
     For Metric   W1- **Fixed: 0910 X 1220 mm**

3.   Name of the file to be saved -
      For Imperial   **c05_Club_ex2**
      For Metric   **M_c05_Club_ex2**

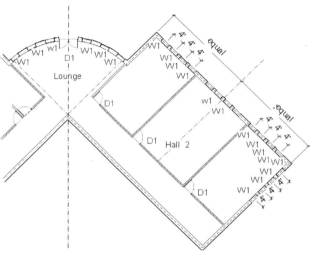

Figure 5-28 *Sketch plan for adding windows to Hall 2 of the Club project*

Chapter 6

Working with Datum Plane and Creating Standard Views

Learning Objectives

After completing this chapter, you will be able to:
• *Understand the concept of levels*
• *Create multiple levels in a project*
• *Understand the concept of using grids in a project*
• *Create a plan view in a project*

WORKING WITH LEVELS

For a multistory building project, you need to specify floor levels within the building volume. Each floor level or story can contain a different set of building components. Levels, in a typical multistory building, may be understood as infinite horizontal planes that define each story. Revit uses levels as references for level-hosted elements such as floor, roof, and ceiling. The distance between levels can be used to define the story-height of a building model, as shown in Figure 6-1. Revit also provides flexibility to create a non-story level or a reference level such as sill level, parapet level, and so on. For example, a multistory office building may have different story heights for each floor. Building components such as exterior walls, windows, doors, and furniture may also differ on each floor. You can create levels based on the story height of a building. You can then create various building elements on each level such as an entrance door on the first floor level, bay windows on the second floor level, an elevator room on the roof level, and so on.

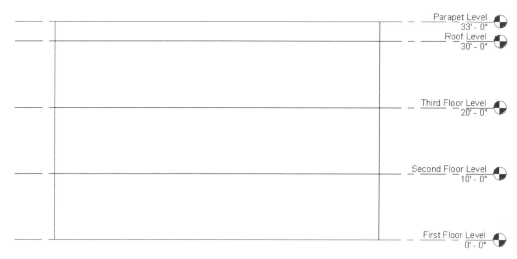

Figure 6-1 *Levels displayed in a multistory building project*

Adding Levels

Ribbon:	Architecture > Datum > Level
Shortcut Key:	LL

In Revit, you can create multiple levels based on your project requirements. Note that the **Level** tool remains inactive in the **Datum** panel for all the plan views. The **Level** tool will only be active in an elevation or a section view. To create a level, invoke the **Level** tool from the **Datum** panel, as shown in Figure 6-1; the **Modify | Place Level** tab will be displayed. In this tab, choose any of the sketching options displayed in the **Draw** panel to create levels in your project. You can also invoke the **Level** tool by typing **LL**. In the **Modify | Place Level** tab, you can select a type of level from the **Type Selector** drop-down list to modify an existing level. This drop-down list has two types of levels, **Level: 1/4" Head** and **Level: No Head**. To make the level head visible, select the **Level: 1/4" Head** option. Else, select the **Level: No Head** option.

WORKING WITH GRIDS

Ribbon: Architecture > Datum > Grid
Shortcut Key: GR

Autodesk Revit provides you the option of creating rectangular or circular grids for your projects. Using these grids, you cannot only create building profiles easily but also place the structural elements at the specific locations and intersections.

Creating Grids

You can create the grid patterns based on the project requirements. Grid patterns can be rectangular or radial, depending on the project geometry. A rectangular grid pattern can be created using straight grid lines, whereas a radial grid pattern can be formed using arc grids. The created grids are visible in all plan, elevation, and section views.

To create a grid line, invoke the **Grid** tool from the **Datum** panel of the **Architecture** tab, as shown in Figure 6-2; the **Modify | Place Grid** tab and the **Properties** palette with the properties of grids will be displayed. The **Modify | Place Grid** tab, as shown in Figure 6-3, displays various options to draw and modify grids in a drawing. The **Draw** panel in this tab displays various tools to draw grids as lines and curves or to convert existing model lines into grids. In this **Properties** palette, you can modify the type and instance properties of the grid, before or after creating it. You can also change the type of grid by selecting a grid type from the **Type Selector** drop-down list.

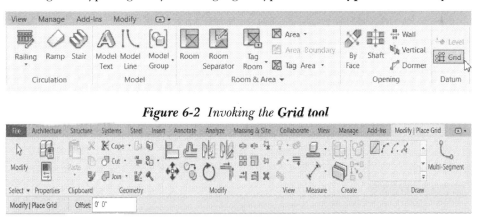

*Figure 6-2 Invoking the **Grid tool***

*Figure 6-3 Various options in the **Modify / Place Grid** tab*

WORKING WITH PROJECT VIEWS

While working on the building model, you may need to view its different exterior and interior portions in order to add or edit the elements in the design. Revit provides various features and techniques that can be used to view the building model. In this section, you will recapitulate some concepts introduced earlier and also learn about the tools that will help you in working with the views.

TUTORIALS

Tutorial 1   Apartment 1

In this tutorial, you will add levels and grids to the *c05_Apartment1_tut1.rvt (M_c05_Apartment1_tut1.rvt* for Metric) project. Also, you will create wall elevation for the kitchen walls and sections using the Figure 6-4 as reference. Do not create the dimensions and text as they have been given only for your reference. Use the following project parameters:

(Expected time: 30 min)

1. Rename Level 1 as **First Floor** and Level 2 as **Second Floor**

2. Levels to be added:
     For Imperial   **Third Floor- Elevation 20'0"**
                              Fourth Floor- Elevation 30'0"
                              Roof Floor- Elevation 40'0"
     For Metric   **Third Floor- Elevation 6000 mm**
                              Fourth Floor- Elevation 9000 mm
                              Roof Floor- Elevation 12000 mm
     Note that in the metric template level 2 is at 4000 mm. Change that level to 3000 mm and then add further levels.

3. Grids and sections to be created using Figure 6-4 as reference. The horizontal section to be renamed as **Section X** and the vertical section as **Section Y**.

The following steps are required to complete this tutorial:

a. Open the file created in Chapter 5.
       For Imperial   *c05_Apartment1_tut1.rvt*
       For Metric   *M_c05_Apartment1_tut1.rvt*
b. Add levels using the **Level** tool, refer to Figures 6-5 through 6-8.
c. Add grids using the **Grid** tool, refer to Figures 6-9 through 6-11.
d. Create section views using the **Section** tool, refer to Figures 6-11 and 6-13.
e. Create and view the four interior wall elevations of the kitchen walls, refer to Figures 6-14 and 6-15.
f. Save the project using the **Save As** tool.
       For Imperial   *c06_Apartment1_tut1.rvt*
       For Metric   *M_c06_Apartment1_tut1.rvt*
g. Close the project.

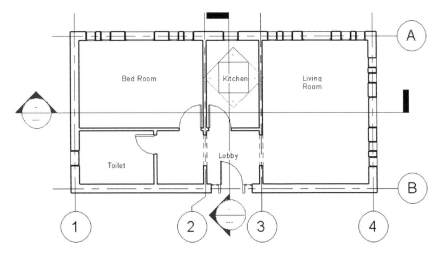

Figure 6-4 Sketch plan for adding grids, sections, and elevations to the Apartment 1 project

Opening an Existing Project and Hiding Tags

Before starting this tutorial, you need to open the specified project, and then you need to hide the door and window tags to simplify the project view using the **Visibility/ Graphics** tool.

1. Choose Open > Project from the File menu and then open the c05_Apartment1_tut1.rvt file (for Metric M_c05_Apartment1_tut1.rvt), created in Tutorial 1 of Chapter 5. You can also download this file from *http://www.cadsofttech.com*. The path of the file is as follows: *Textbooks > Civil/GIS > Revit Architecture > Revit Architecture 2019 For Novices*

2. Ensure that the **Floor Plans** view for Level 1 is opened. Next, to hide the doors and windows tags, choose the **Visibility/ Graphics** tool from the **Graphics** panel of the **View** tab; the **Visibility/ Graphic Overrides for Floor Plan:Level 1** dialog box is displayed.

3. Choose the **Annotation Categories** tab from the dialog box and clear the check boxes for **Door Tags** and **Window Tags**.

4. Choose the **Apply** button to apply the changes and then the **OK** button to close the dialog box and return to the drawing window.

Adding Levels

In this section, you will learn to create levels in the elevation view.

1. Move the cursor to the **Project Browser** and double-click on **North** under the **Elevations (Building Elevation)** head. The north elevation with the existing levels is displayed in the drawing window. Make sure that the **Hidden Line** option is selected in the **Visual Style** menu of the **View Control Bar**. Select the levels and drag the endpoints of the level lines near the building profile; the view is adjusted, as shown in Figure 6-5.

Figure 6-5 *The north elevation view of the Apartment 1 project*

2. Invoke the **Level** tool from the **Datum** panel of the **Architecture** tab.

 Note

*In the metric unit system, by default, the Level 2 is at 4000 mm. Shift the Level 2 to 3000 mm by clicking on the value and entering the value as **3000**.*

3. Next, move the cursor near the left endpoint of the level line of Level 2 and then move it upward and when the alignment line appears, enter **10'0"(3000 mm)** as the distance of the new level from the Level 2, as shown in Figure 6-6.

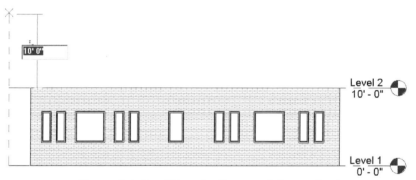

Figure 6-6 *Specifying the distance of the new level*

4. Move the cursor toward right until the alignment line is displayed above the Level 2 bubble, as shown in Figure 6-7, and click to complete the level line. The new level line is created showing the level name as **Level 3**, and the elevation as **20'0"(6000 mm)**. Press ESC to exit.

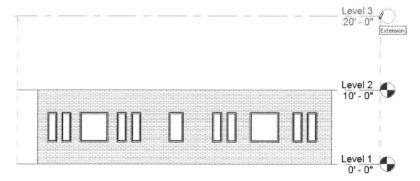

Figure 6-7 *Creating the new level line using the alignment line*

5. Repeat the procedure followed in steps 3 and 4 to create two more levels, Level 4 and Level 5 above Level 3 at a distance of **10'0"(3000 mm)** each. Press ESC twice to exit the **Level** tool.

   Notice that the **Project Browser** now shows the floor and ceiling plans for Level 3, Level 4, and Level 5.

6. To rename the levels, move the cursor over Level 1 under the **Floor Plans** head in the **Project Browser** and then right-click to display a shortcut menu.

7. Choose the **Rename** option from the shortcut menu; the edit box is displayed.

8. Enter **First Floor** in the edit box and choose the **OK** button. Autodesk Revit asks whether you want to rename the corresponding levels and views.

9. Choose the **Yes** button to rename the levels and views. Level 1 is renamed to **First Floor** in the elevation view.

10. Repeat the procedure followed in steps 6 through 9 to rename Level 2 as **Second Floor**, Level 3 as **Third Floor**, Level 4 as **Fourth Floor**, and Level 5 as **Roof**. Figure 6-8 shows all levels renamed in the north elevation.

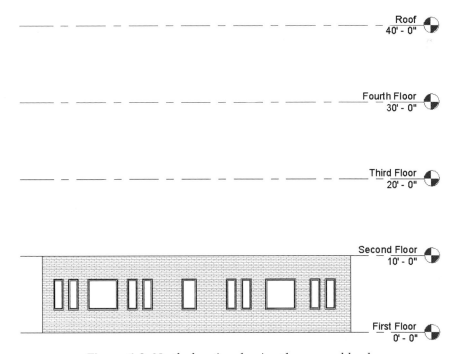

Figure 6-8 *North elevation showing the renamed levels*

Adding Grid Lines

You can use the plan view to add grids to the project using the **Grid** tool. Grids are automatically numbered as they are created. You will create grids in the sequence, as shown in the sketch plan.

1.   Double-click on **First Floor** from the **Floor Plans** head in the **Project Browser** to display the ground floor plan in the drawing window.

2.   Next, choose the **Grid** tool from the **Datum** panel of the **Architecture** tab; the **Modify | Place Grid** tab is displayed.

     Notice that the sketch plan shows the grid lines as the centerlines of walls. You can use the **Line** tool (default) from the **Draw** panel to create them.

3.   Now, ensure that the **Line** tool is chosen in the **Draw** panel.

4.   Move the cursor near the top left corner of the exterior wall profile and move the cursor up till a vertical extension line is displayed. Click to specify the start point of the grid line when the temporary dimension of 3'0"(900 mm) is displayed from the centerline of the exterior wall, as shown in Figure 6-9.

5.   Move the cursor vertically downward and click outside the south wall to specify the endpoint of the grid line, as shown in Figure 6-10.

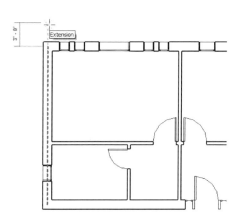

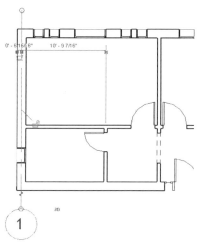

Figure 6-9 Specifying the start point of the grid line

Figure 6-10 Specifying the end point of the first vertical grid line

Note
*If grid lines are not visible in the drawing, choose the **Visibility/ Graphics** tool from the **Graphics** panel of the **View** tab to display the **Visibility/ Graphic Overrides for Floor Plan** dialog box. In the **Annotation Categories** tab of this dialog box, select the **Grids** check box.*

The same procedure can be followed to draw grid lines for the interior walls. As the thickness of the interior wall is 5"(127 mm), you can specify 2 1/2"(64 mm) as the offset distance to draw grid lines for the interior walls.

6.   Repeat the procedure followed in steps 3, 4, and 5 to create other vertical and horizontal grid lines in the sequence of their numbers using the alignment line feature. After adding grid lines, press ESC twice to exit. Figure 6-11 shows the floor plan after adding grid lines.

7. To rename the grid 5, select it and then click on its name. The edit box with the current number is displayed.

8. Enter the value **A** in the edit box and press ENTER to rename the grid.

9. Repeat steps 7 and 8 to rename the grid 6 as **B**.

 Note

*You can rename a grid by selecting it from the drawing and then entering a value corresponding to the value column for the **Name** parameter in the **Properties** palette. The entered value will be the new name of the grid.*

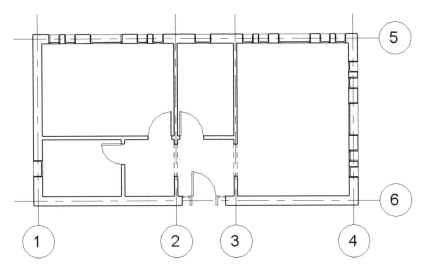

Figure 6-11 The horizontal and vertical grids created for the wall centerlines

Creating Section Views

The Section views can be created by using the **Section** tool.

1. Choose the **Section** tool from the **Create** panel of the **View** tab.

2. Move the cursor near the midpoint of the west wall. Click to specify the start point of the section line, refer to Figure 6-12.

3. Move the cursor horizontally across the building plan until you cross the exterior face of the east wall, as shown in Figure 6-12. Click to specify the endpoint of the section line. The section view is created and the name **Section 1** is displayed in the **Sections (Building Section)** head in the **Project Browser**.

4. Repeat the procedure followed in steps 2 and 3 to create a transverse section through the apartment building, as shown in Figure 6-13. Choose a point outside the main entrance as the start point and move the cursor vertically upward beyond the exterior wall of the kitchen to specify the endpoint of the section line. As the bubble of the grid line 2 touches the section line, you can move the grid bubble using the **Modify the grid by dragging its model end** tool.

5. Select the grid line 2 and click on the **Add elbow** symbol displayed near the grid bubble.

6. Drag the two blue dots to a location outside the exterior wall, refer to Figure 6-13. Press ESC to exit.

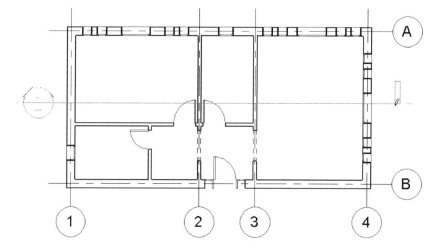

Figure 6-12   *Creating a section line for the section view*

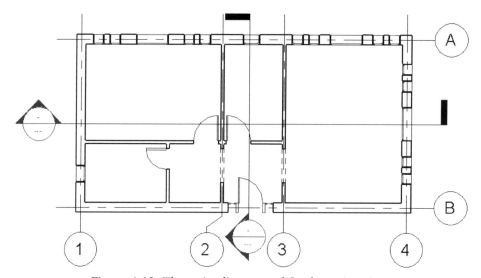

Figure 6-13   *The section lines created for the section views*

7. Click on the '**+**' symbol on the left of the **Sections (Building Section)** head in the **Project Browser** to display the section name created. Right-click on **Section 1** and then choose **Rename** from the shortcut menu; the edit box is displayed.

8. Enter **Section X** in the edit box and then choose **OK**; the section view is renamed.

9. Similarly, rename **Section 2** as **Section Y**.

10. Double-click on **Section X** to display the corresponding section in the drawing window, as shown in Figure 6-14.

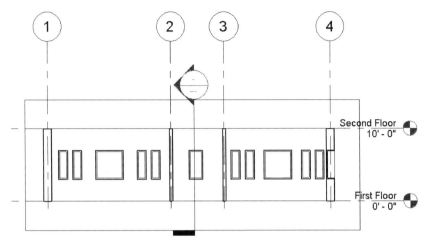

Figure 6-14 Section view of **Section X**

Creating Elevation Views

To create the interior wall elevation of the kitchen walls, use the **Elevation** tool. You can use the first floor plan view to create new elevations.

1. Double-click on the name **First Floor** in the **Floor Plans** head of the **Project Browser** to display the first floor plan in the drawing window.

2. Choose the **Elevation** tool from **View > Create > Elevation** drop-down.

3. Move the cursor and place on a wall near the door in the kitchen area until the arrowhead points upward, toward the kitchen window and click to create the elevation.

4. Press the ESC key twice to exit the **Elevation** tool.

5. Select the elevation symbol to display its controls.

6. Click to select all the three cleared check boxes to create interior elevations. The new elevations are added under the **Elevations (Building Elevation)** head in the **Project Browser**.

7. Right-click the elevation views 1-a , 1-b , 1-c , and 1-d and using the corresponding shortcut menus, rename them as Kitchen-North Wall, Kitchen-East Wall, Kitchen-South Wall, and Kitchen-West Wall, respectively .

8. Double-click on the **Kitchen-North Wall** option in the **Project Browser** to display the corresponding elevation view. The crop-region can be picked by selecting the box. On selecting the box, drag controls appear. Drag the view crop region using the drag controls and grids of the kitchen area, as shown in Figure 6-15. Similarly, create the **Kitchen- South Wall** elevation, as shown in Figure 6-16.

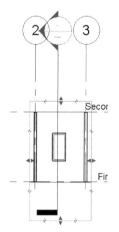

Figure 6-15 *The Kitchen-North Wall elevation*

Figure 6-16 *The Kitchen-South Wall elevation*

  Note
*If the crop-region boundary is not visible in the drawing, then choose the **Show Crop Region** button from the **View Control Bar**.*

9. Double-click on **First Floor** under the **Floor Plans** head in the **Project Browser** to return to the floor plan view.

Saving the Project

In this section, you will save the project file using the **Save As** tool.

1. Choose **Save As > Project** from the **File** menu; the **Save As** dialog box is displayed. Enter **c06_Apartment1_tut1** in the **File name** edit box and then choose **Save** to save the project.

2. Choose the **Close** option from the **File** menu.

Tutorial 2   Club

In this tutorial, you will add levels and grids to the *c05_Club_ex2.rvt (M_c05_Club_ex2.rvt)* project created in Exercise 2 of Chapter 5. Also, you will create sections in the sketch plan shown in Figure 6-17. Do not create dimensions and texts as they have been given only for reference. Use the following project parameter.   **(Expected time: 30 min)**

1. Rename Level 1 as the **First Floor** and move the Roof level to **15'0"(4572 mm)** elevation. Rename the Level 2 as **Roof** in Metric unit system.

2. Grids and sections to be created in the sketch plan are shown in Figure 6-17.

    The following steps are required to complete this tutorial:

a. Open the file.
   For Imperial   *c05_Club_ex2.rvt*
   For Metric   *M_c05_Club_ex2.rvt*
b. Modify levels by dragging, refer to Figures 6-18 and 6-19.
c. Add grids using the **Grid** tool, refer to Figures 6-20 and 6-21.
d. Create section views using the **Section** tool, refer to Figure 6-22 through Figure 6-24.
e. Save the project using the **Save As** tool.
   For Imperial   *c06_Club_tut2.rvt*
   For Metric   *M_c06_Club_tut2.rvt*
f. Close the project.

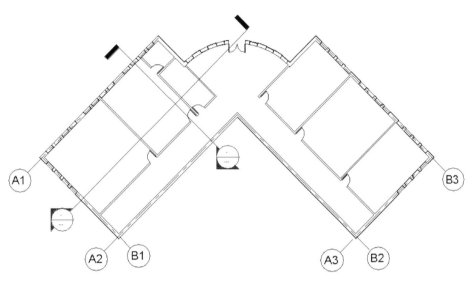

Figure 6-17 Sketch plan for adding grids and creating section views for the Club project

Opening the Existing Project and Hiding Tags

To start with the tutorial, you need to open the Club project file and hide the door and window tags using the **Visibility/ Graphics** tool.

1. Choose **Open > Project** from the **File** menu and open the required file.
   For Imperial   *c05_Club_ex2.rvt*
   For Metric   *M_c05_Club_ex2.rvt*
   You can also download this file from *http://www.cadsofttech.com*. The path of the file is as follows: *Textbooks > Civil/GIS > Revit Architecture > Revit Architecture 2019 For Novices*

2. Choose the **Visibility/ Graphics** tool from the **Graphics** panel of the **View** tab; the **Visibility/ Graphics Overrides for Floor Plan** dialog box for the plan view is displayed.

3. Choose the **Annotations Categories** tab and clear the check boxes for **Door Tags** and **Window Tags**.

4. In the **Visibility/ Graphic Overrides for Floor plan** dialog box, choose the **Apply** and **OK** buttons to apply the changes and close it.

Modifying Levels

You can use the **Elevation** tool to display any exterior elevation of the project. You will open the north elevation and then drag the level to the specified distance.

1. Move the cursor to the **Project Browser** and double-click on **North** under the **Elevations (Building Elevation)** head. The north elevation is displayed within the existing levels in the drawing window.

2. Choose the **Zoom In Region** tool from the **Navigation Bar** to enlarge the right portion of the elevation showing the levels, as shown in Figure 6-18. Ensure that the **Hidden Line** option is chosen in the **View Control Bar** for Visual Style.

   Notice that the wall extends beyond the roof level line. This is because you have used the explicit parameter for the wall height. You can now move the level to the wall top.

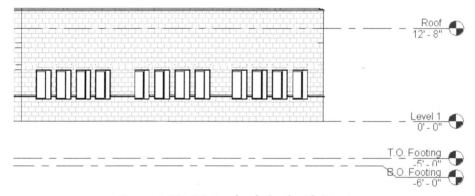

Figure 6-18 *Existing levels for the Club project*

3. Move the cursor near the roof level line and click when it gets highlighted. Drag it to the top of the wall. The elevation in the level bubble now shows **15' - 0"** (**4572 mm** for Metric) as its elevation from the base.

4. To rename the levels, move the cursor over **Level 1** in the **Project Browser** and right-click; a shortcut menu is displayed.

5. Choose the **Rename** option from the shortcut menu; the **edit** box is displayed.

6. In this dialog box, enter **First Floor** in the edit box. Next, choose the **OK** button. You are prompted to verify whether you want to rename the corresponding levels and views.

7. Choose the **Yes** button to rename the levels and views. The level is immediately renamed in the elevation view, as shown in Figure 6-19.

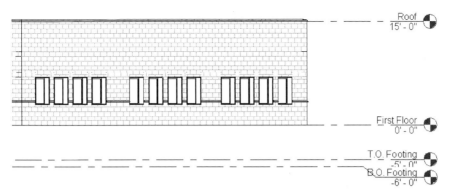

Figure 6-19 *Renamed levels and views for the Club project*

Similarly, rename the level 2 as **Roof** in the Metric unit system.

Creating Grid Lines

You will use the plan view to add grids to the project using the **Grid** tool. The grids are automatically numbered as they are created. You will, however, rename them based on the names given in the sketch plan.

1. Double-click on **First Floor** from the **Floor Plans** head of the **Project Browser** to display the first floor plan in the drawing window.

2. Choose the **Grid** tool from the **Datum** panel of the **Architecture** tab.

    Notice that the sketch plan shows the grid lines as the centerlines of the walls. Use the **Line** tool to create grid lines at the centerline of the walls. You may need to zoom into the area for Revit to snap to the wall centerlines.

3. Choose the Line tool if not chosen by default in the **Draw** panel of the **Modify | Place Grid** tab.

4. Zoom into the west corner of Hall 1 and move the cursor near the exterior wall intersection, marked 1, refer to Figure 6-20. Use the TAB key to toggle between the object snaps at the intersection and click when a dashed line appears in the center of the wall on which the grid 1 is to be created, refer to Figure 6-20.

5. Move the cursor along the exterior wall and click when the cursor crosses the lower exterior wall intersection, as shown in Figure 6-20. The first grid line is created.

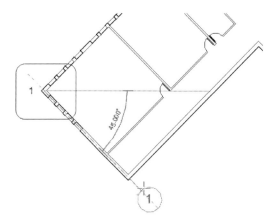

Figure 6-20 *Grid line created using the* **Line** *tool in the* **Draw** *panel*

6. Repeat the procedure followed in steps 4 and 5 to create other grid lines for the external walls, as shown in the Figure 6-21. Press ESC twice to exit.

    The completed plan with grids will be similar to the one shown in Figure 6-21.

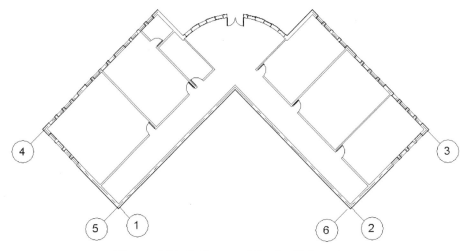

Figure 6-21 *Grids created for the Club project*

7. Double-click on grid number 4; an edit box with the current grid number is displayed.

8. Enter **A1** in the edit box to rename the grid.

9. Repeat the procedure followed in steps 7 and 8 to rename all other grid numbers based on the sketch plan, refer to Figure 6-17.

Creating Section Views

The Section views can be created by using the **Section** tool.

1. Choose the **Section** tool from the **Create** panel of the **View** tab.

2. Move the cursor over the wall of the grid A1, refer to Figure 6-22 and drag it downward to specify start point of the section line. Now, drag it straight to draw a section across the building, refer to Figure 6-22.

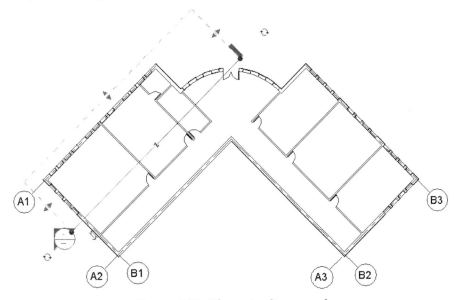

Figure 6-22 *The section line created*

3. Move the cursor diagonally upward across the building plan until you cross the exterior face of the lobby wall. Click to specify the endpoint of the section line, as shown in Figure 6-22. The name, **Section 1** is displayed in the **Sections (Building Sections)** head in the **Project Browser**.

4. Repeat the procedure followed in steps 2 and 3 to create a transverse section through Hall 1 of the club building, as shown in Figure 6-23.

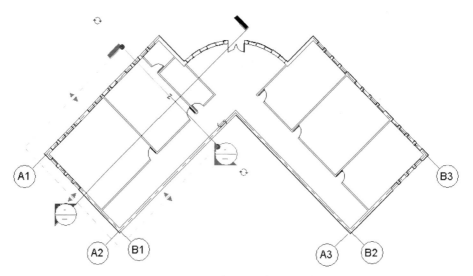

Figure 6-23 *Creating the second section line*

5. Right-click on the name **Section 1** under the **Section (Building Section)** in the **Project Browser**, and then choose the **Rename** option from the shortcut menu displayed; the edit box is displayed.

6. In edit box, enter **Section X** in the edit box and choose the **OK** button.

7. Repeat the procedure followed in steps 5 and 6 to rename **Section 2** as **Section Y**, as specified in the sketch plan.

8. Double-click on **Section X** in the **Project Browser** to display the corresponding section in the drawing window, as shown in Figure 6-24.

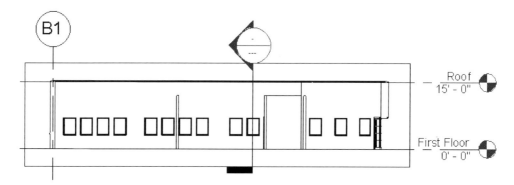

Figure 6-24 *Displaying the section view for the Club project*

9. Double-click on **First Floor** under the **Floor Plans** head in the **Project Browser** to display the floor plan of the first floor.

Saving the Project

In this section, you will save the project file using the **Save As** tool.

1. Choose **Save As > Project** from the **File** menu and enter the required name **c06 _Club_tut2** (for Metric **M_c06 _Club_tut2**) in the **File name** edit box of the **Save As** dialog box. Next, choose the **Save** button.

2. Choose **Close** from the **File** menu to close the file.

EXERCISES

Exercise 1   Apartment 2

Add levels and grids to the *c05_Apartment2_ex1.rvt* (*M_c05_Apartment2_ex1.rvt* for Metric) project created in Exercise 1 of Chapter 5. Create the wall elevation for the dining room walls and also sections in the sketch plan shown in Figure 6-25. Do not create dimensions and texts as they are given only for your reference. Use the parameters given below.

(Expected time: 30 min)

1. Rename Level 1 as the **First Floor** and Level 2 as the **Second Floor**.
   In Metric unit system, shift the Level 2 to **3000** mm.
2. Levels to be added:
   For Imperial   **Third Floor- Elevation 20'0"**
                            Fourth Floor- Elevation 30'0"
                            Roof- Elevation 40'0"
   For Metric   **Third Floor- Elevation 6000 mm**
                            Fourth Floor- Elevation 9000 mm
                            Roof- Elevation 12000 mm
3. Grids and Sections to be created in the sketch plan shown in Figure 6-25. Name the horizontal section as **Section X1** and the vertical section as **Section Y1.**
4. Name of the file to be save-
   For Imperial   **c06_Apartment2_ex1**
   For Metric   **M_c06_Apartment2_ex1**

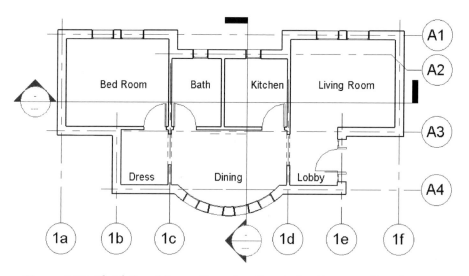

Figure 6-25 *Sketch for adding grids and sections to the Apartment 2 project*

Chapter 7

Using Basic Building Components-II

Learning Objectives

After completing this chapter, you will be able to:

• *Understand the concept of floor*
• *Create floors using the Floor tool*
• *Create roofs using the Roof tool*
• *Create rooms using the Room tool*

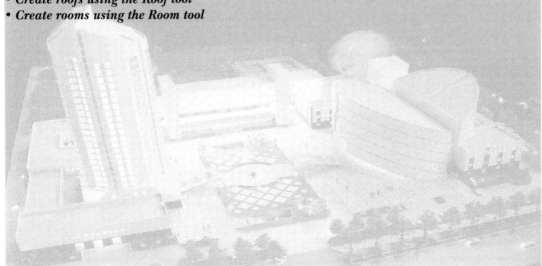

CREATING ARCHITECTURAL FLOORS

Ribbon: Architecture > Build > Floor drop-down > Floor: Architectural

You can add a floor to the current level of a building model using the **Floor: Architectural** tool. You can invoke this tool from the **Build** panel of the **Architecture** tab. On invoking this tool, the **Modify | Create Floor Boundary** contextual tab will be displayed, as shown in Figure 7-1.

Figure 7-1 The Modify / Create Floor Boundary tab

CREATING ROOFS

A roof is a structure that covers the uppermost part of a building. The primary function of a roof is to protect the building and its contents from rain. The other functions of a roof depend upon the nature of the structure that it is protecting. For dwellings, a roof can protect against heat, cold, sunlight, and wind.

In Autodesk Revit, you can create a roof structure using various tools displayed in the **Roof** drop-down in the **Build** panel of the **Architecture** tab, as shown in Figure 7-2. You can use the extrusions or mass instances present in the drawing to create a roof.

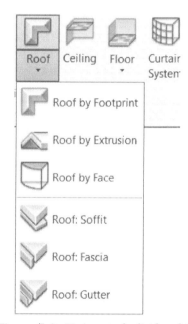

Figure 7-2 Various tools displayed in the Roof drop-down

ROOMS

Room is a part of Autodesk Revit building elements. Autodesk Revit provides you the flexibility of creating rooms independent of room tags. Rooms can be created only in the plan view. You can also add rooms from the room schedules. Rooms and areas have the same graphical representation.

Adding Rooms

Ribbon: Architecture > Room & Area > Room

You can add rooms to the plan view by using the **Room** tool. To do so, invoke this tool from the **Room & Area** panel; the **Modify|Place Room** tab will be displayed. You can place the room tag by clicking on the room bounded by the elements.

TUTORIALS

Tutorial 1   Apartment 1

In this tutorial, you will add a floor and a ceiling to the *c06_Apartment1_tut1.rvt* project created in Tutorial 1 of Chapter 6. Also, you will attach walls to the floor. To complete this tutorial, you need to use the following project parameters: **(Expected time: 30 min)**

1. Floor type -
        For Imperial   **Floor: LW Concrete on Metal Deck**.
        For Metric   **160mm Concrete With 50mm Metal Deck**
2. Ceiling type-
        For Imperial   **Compound Ceiling: GWB on Mtl. Stud**,
        For Metric   **Compound Ceiling: Plain**
   Level- 8'6" from the floor level.

The following steps are required to complete this tutorial:

a. Open the required file.
b. Hide the annotation tags such as the section line, grids, and the elevation tag.
c. Create the floor using the **Floor** tool, refer to Figures 7-3 through 7-5.
d. Create the ceiling using the **Ceiling** tool, refer to Figures 7-6 and 7-7.
e. Attach walls to the floor.
f. Save the project using the **Save As** tool.
        For Imperial   *c07_Apartment1_tut1.rvt*
        For Metric   *M_c07_Apartment1_tut1.rvt*
g. Close the project.

Opening the Project File and Hiding Annotation Tags

To start with this tutorial, open the specified project file and then hide the annotation symbols and tags such as section line, grids, and elevation tags using the **Visibility/Graphics** tool.

1. Choose **Open > Project** from the **File** menu and then open the *c06_Apartment1_tut1.rvt* (*M_c06_Apartment1_tut1.rvt* for Metric) file created in Tutorial 1 of Chapter 6. You can also download this file from *http://www.cadsofttech.com*. The path of the file is as follows: *Textbooks > Civil/GIS > Revit Architecture> Revit Architecture 2019 for Novices*

2. Double click on **First Floor plan** from **Floor Plans** head in the project browser, If not displyed by default. Choose the **Visibility/Graphics** tool from the **Graphics** panel of the **View** tab; the **Visibility/Graphics Overrides for Floor Plan: First Floor** dialog box is displayed.

3. Choose the **Annotation Categories** tab and clear the check boxes under the **Visibility** parameter for **Elevations**, **Grids**, and **Sections**.

4. Now, choose the **Apply** button and then the **OK** button; the specified settings are applied to the plan view and you return to the drawing window.

Creating the Floor

In the following set of steps, you will add floor to the apartment plan using the **Floor** tool.

1. Choose the **Floor: Architectural** tool from **Architecture > Build > Floor** drop-down; the **Modify | Create Floor Boundary** tab is displayed along with the **Options Bar**. Notice that the drawing area fades when you invoke the **Floor** tool, which indicates that you are in the sketch mode.

2. In the **Options Bar**, select the **Extend into wall (to core)** check box, if it is not selected. Also notice that the **Pick Walls** tool is chosen by default in the **Draw** panel.

3. Move the cursor near the center of the north wall of the apartment plan, and press the TAB key when the wall is highlighted.

4. When the chain of walls is highlighted, click to sketch the floor boundary; the boundary is sketched and appears as a magenta rectangle, as shown in Figure 7-3.

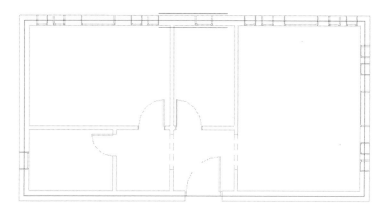

*Figure 7-3 The floor boundary sketched using the **Pick Walls** tool*

5. Choose the **Finish Edit Mode** button from the **Mode** panel to complete the sketching of the floor.

6. Next, you need to assign the type to the floor.

    Select the option from the **Type Selector** drop-down list in the **Properties** palette, as shown in Figure 7-4.

    For Imperial **Floor : LW Concrete on Metal Deck**
    For Metric   **160mm Concrete With 50mm Metal Deck**

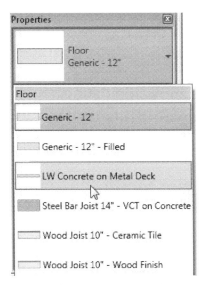

Figure 7-4 *Selecting the **LW** **Concrete on Metal Deck** floor type*

7. Choose the **Modify** button from the **Select** panel of the **Modify | Floor** tab to exit the **Floor: Architectural** tool. The floor is created for the *Apartment 1* project, as shown in Figure 7-5.

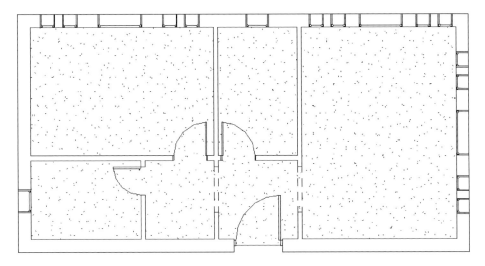

Figure 7-5 *The **LW Concrete on Metal Deck** type of the floor created*

Creating the Ceiling

After creating the floor for the apartment, you need to add a ceiling to it. For this you need to transform the current view to the ceiling plan view.

1. Double-click on **First Floor** from the **Ceiling Plans** head in the **Project Browser**.

As you open this view, you will notice the appearance of the annotation tags. Repeat steps 2, 3, and 4 given in the **Opening the Project File and Hiding Annotation Tags** section in this tutorial to hide various grids, elevation, window, and section tags from the first floor ceiling plan view.

2. Invoke the **Ceiling** tool from the **Build** panel of the **Architecture** tab; the **Modify | Place Ceiling** tab is displayed.

3. Click on the **Type Selector** drop-down list in the **Properties** palette and then select the desired option from it.

> For Imperial   **Compound Ceiling : GWB on Mtl. Stud**
> For Metric   **Compound Ceiling : Plain**

Next, you need to define the clear height of the ceiling.

4. In the **Properties** palette, click on the value field of the **Height Offset From Level** instance parameter and enter **8'6"(2590 mm)**. Then, choose the **Apply** button; the new height is assigned to the ceiling.

5. Move the cursor inside any room; the room boundary is highlighted. Now, click inside the highlighted boundary area; the ceiling is created. Notice that the created ceiling is not distinctly visible in the ceiling plan because the ceiling type selected has a plain GWB board finish.

6. Repeat step 5 to create individual ceilings for every room in the *Apartment 1* project. After creating all the ceilings, press ESC twice to view them in the 3D view of the project.

7. Click on the + symbol for the **3D Views** head in the **Project Browser** and double-click on **{3D}**; the 3D view of the apartment project with the created ceiling is displayed. You can move the cursor over the ceiling of any room to highlight it and display the ceiling type, as shown in Figure 7-6.

Attaching Walls to the Floor

In this section, you will use the **Attach** tool to attach walls to the floor so that you get a clear intersection between the floor and the wall. You need to use the section view to attach the floor.

1. Double-click on **Section X** in the **Project Browser**.

2. Now, move the cursor near the external wall that is cut in the section, and when it is highlighted, press TAB to highlight all the exterior walls.

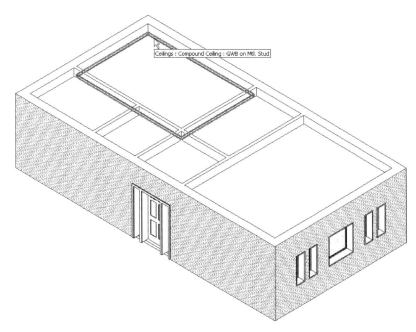

Figure 7-6 Highlighting and displaying the ceiling type for bedroom

3. Click to select the chain of exterior walls in the section view and then choose the **Attach Top/Base** tool from the **Modify Wall** panel of the **Modify | Walls** tab; the **Options Bar** is displayed.

4. From the **Options Bar**, select the **Base** radio button.

5. Move the cursor near the floor and click when it is highlighted; the floor is attached to walls, as shown in Figure 7-7.

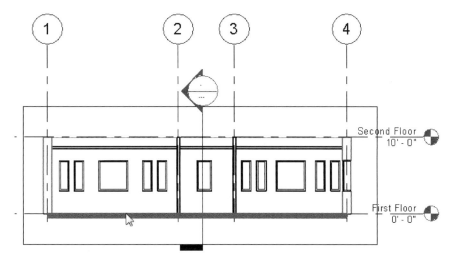

Figure 7-7 Selecting the floor to attach it with the exterior walls

6. Double-click on **First Floor** in the **Floor Plans** head in the **Project Browser**; the corresponding floor plan in the drawing window is displayed.

 Note

*In this section of the tutorial, as you attach walls with the floor, you may not find any difference in the wall and the floor intersections as compared to when they were not attached. To see the difference, attach the wall with the floor and then enter a positive value in the value column corresponding to the **Height Offset From Level** instance parameter in the **Properties** Palette of the selected floor.*

Saving the Project

In this section, you will save the project file using the **Save As** tool.

1. Choose **Save As > Project** from the **File** menu; the **Save As** dialog box is displayed. Enter required name in the **File name** edit box

       For Imperial   **c07_Apartment1_tut1**
       For Metric   **M_c07_Apartment1_tut1**

Choose **Save**; the project file is saved.

2. Now, choose **Close** from the **File** menu to close the file.

Tutorial 2   Club

In this tutorial, you will add a floor, ceiling, and a roof to the *Club* project created in Tutorial 2 of Chapter 6. In this tutorial, you will also attach floor and ceilings to walls. Figure 7-8 shows a 3D View of the *Club* project after adding roofs and other elements. Use the following project parameters to complete this tutorial: **(Expected time: 30 min)**

1. Floor type -
       For Imperial   **LW Concrete on Metal Deck**.
       For Metric   **160mm Concrete With 50mm Metal Deck**
2. Ceiling type-
       For Imperial   **Compound Ceiling: 2'x 2' ACT System**
       For Metric   **Compound Ceiling: 600 x 600 mm Grid**
   Level- 11'0" from floor level.
3. Roof type for Hall 1 and Hall 2- Hip roof-
       For Imperial   **Basic Roof: Insulation on Metal Deck-EPDM**
       For Metric   **Basic Roof: Steel Bar Joist Steel Deck- EPDM Membrane**
   Roof shape for Hall 1 and Hall 2- Hip roof with Slope as 4"/12" (8.46 mm)
   Roof level for Hall 1 and Hall 2- Roof
   Roof type for Lounge-
       For Imperial   **Basic Roof: Insulation on Metal Deck - EPDM**
       For Metric   **Basic Roof: Steel Deck-EPDM Membrane**

   Roof shape for Lounge- Flat
   Roof level for Lounge- **Roof**; Base Offset from level **-1'4"(406 mm)**
   Overhang for all roofs- 4'0" (1220 mm) from the outer face of the exterior walls
   The following steps are required to complete this tutorial:

a.   Open the required project file.
         For Imperial   *c06_Club_tut2.rvt*
         For Metric   *M_c06_Club_tut2.rvt*
b.   Hide the annotation tags such as section line, grids, and elevation tag.
c.   Create the floor using the **Floor** tool, refer to Figure 7-9
d.   Create the ceiling using the **Ceiling** tool.
e.   Create the roof using the **Roof by Footprint** tool, refer to Figures 7-10 through 7-16.
f.   Attach all walls to the floor.
g.   Save the project using the **Save As** tool.
         For Imperial   *c07_Club_tut2.rvt*
         For Metric   *M_c07_Club_tut2.rvt*
h.   Close the project.

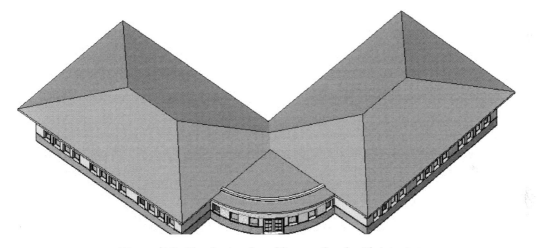

Figure 7-8 *Sketch view for adding roof to the Club project*

Opening the Project File and Hiding Annotation Tags

In this section, you will open the *Club* project that was created in Tutorial 2 of Chapter 6 and then hide annotation symbols and tags before you start creating floor, ceiling, and roof in the next section.

1.   Choose **Open > Project** from the **File** menu and then open the *c06_Club_tut2.rvt* (*M_c06_Club_tut2.rvt* for Metric) file created in Tutorial 2 of Chapter 6. You can also download this file from *http://www.cadsofttech.com*. The path of the file is as follows: *Textbooks > Civil/GIS > Revit Architecture > Revit Architecture 2019 for Novices*

2.   After the specified file is opened, ensure that the **First Floor** for the **Floor Plans** is the current view selected and then choose the **Visibility/ Graphics** tool from the **Graphics** panel of the **View** tab; the **Visibility/Graphic Overrides for Floor Plan: First Floor** dialog box is displayed.

3.   Select the **Annotation Categories** tab to open annotation categories.

4.   Clear the check boxes under the **Visibility** parameter for **Elevations**, **Grids**, and **Sections** in the dialog box.

5. Choose **Apply** and then **OK** to apply the settings to the plan view and close the dialog box to return to the drawing window.

Creating the Floor

In the following steps, you will add a floor to the club plan using the **Floor** tool.

1. Invoke the **Floor: Architectural** tool from **Architecture > Build > Floor** drop-down; the **Modify | Create Floor Boundary** tab is displayed.

2. Ensure that the **Pick Walls** tool is chosen in the **Draw** panel. Clear the **Extend into wall (to core)** check box in the **Options Bar**.

3. Move the cursor near any exterior wall of the club building plan until it gets highlighted. When the exterior wall is highlighted, press the TAB key; all the exterior walls get highlighted and dashed lines appear in the walls indicating the extents of the floor.

4. When the chain of walls is highlighted, click to sketch the floor boundary. Ensure that the floor boundary line is sketched on the outer face of the exterior wall, as shown in Figure 7-9. If required, use the flip control to move the floor profile to the outer face

Note
While sketching the floor boundary, make sure it is in a closed loop. Else, a warning message will be displayed and the floor will not be created.

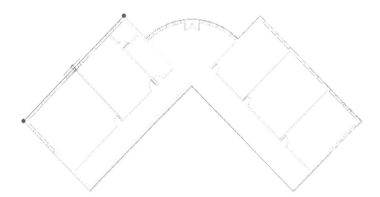

Figure 7-9 *The sketched floor boundary*

5. Now, finish the sketch of the floor by choosing the **Finish Edit Mode** button from the **Mode** panel.

6. Next, you need to assign a type to the floor.

    In the **Properties** palette, select the desired option from the **Type Selector** drop-down list. Ignore the warning, if displayed.

    For Imperial   **LW Concrete on Metal Deck**
    For Metric   **160mm Concrete With 50mm Metal Deck**

To exit from the **Floor: Architectural** tool, choose the **Modify** button from the **Select** panel.

Creating the Ceiling

In this section, you will add ceiling to the *Club* project in the ceiling plan using the **Ceiling** tool.

1. First you need to change the project view to the ceiling plan. To do so, Double-click on the **First Floor** from the **Ceiling Plans** head of the **Project Browser**; the first floor ceiling plan is displayed in the drawing.

2. Now, you need to assign a type to the ceiling. To do so, Invoke the **Ceiling** tool from the **Build** panel of the **Architecture** tab; the properties for the proposed ceiling are displayed in the **Properties** palette.

3. In the **Properties** palette, click on the **Type Selector** drop-down list and select the required option from it.

   For Imperial   **Compound Ceiling: 2' x 2' ACT System**
   For Metric   **Compound Ceiling: 600 x 600mm Grid**

4. Now, you need to assign height to the ceiling.
   In the **Properties** palette, click in the value field of the **Height Offset From Level** instance parameter and enter **11'0"(3353 mm)**. Then, choose the **Apply** button.

5. Now, move the cursor inside the building profile and notice that each space boundary is highlighted, when you move it inside the boundary.

6. Click inside each room to create the ceiling at the specified height. It appears as a square grid in the first floor ceiling plan.

Note
Sketch the ceiling for uneven room.

7. Press ESC to exit from the **Ceiling** tool.

Creating the Roof

In this section, first you will create the hip roof for Hall 1 using the **Roof by Footprint** tool and then similarly create roofs for the Lounge and the Hall 2 areas.

1. First, change the project view to the floor plan of the first floor.
   Double-click on **First Floor** from the **Floor Plans** head of the **Project Browser**; the floor plan of the first floor is displayed.

2. Invoke the **Roof by Footprint** tool from **Architecture > Build > Roof** drop-down.

3. In the **Options Bar**, select the **Defines slope** check box and enter **4'0"** (**1220 mm**) in the **Overhang** edit box.

4. Choose the **Pick Walls** tool, if not chosen, from the **Draw** panel of the **Modify |
   Create Roof Footprint** tab.

5. Move the cursor near the exterior wall of Hall 1, facing northwest, and click when the dashed
   line appears on the outer side, as shown in Figure 7-10. The roof boundary line is sketched.

6. Similarly, create boundary lines by using the other three exterior walls of Hall 1 at the same
   offset distance. The boundary lines are sketched, as shown in Figure 7-11.

Figure 7-10 *Sketching the roof profile*   *Figure 7-11* *Completing the roof profile of Hall1*

7. Next, you need to join the boundary lines marked as C and D, refer to Figure 7-11. To
   do so, choose the **Trim/Extend to Corner** tool from the **Modify** panel of the **Modify |
   Create Roof Footprint** tab and select the two lines marked as C and D to complete the closed
   rectangular profile of the roof of Hall 1. After completing the profile, press the ESC key to
   exit the **Trim/Extend to Corner** tool.

8. In the **Properties** palette, click on the value column for the **Base Level** instance parameter
   and select **Roof** as the base level.

9. Next, click on the value column for the **Base Offset From Level** instance parameter and
   ensure that **0' 0"(0 mm)** is entered as the base level offset value. Then, choose the **Apply**
   button.

   To set appropriate slope for the hip roof, you must select the sketch boundary and then set
   its slope properties.

10. First select one of the four boundary lines, and then select the rest by using the CTRL key; the
    instance properties for the selected boundary lines are displayed in the **Properties** palette.

11. In the **Properties** palette, replace the current value present in the value column of the **Slope**
    instance parameter by entering **4" / 12"(18.46°)** as the new value of the pitch, as specified
    in the project parameters, and then choose the **Apply** button.

12. Next, choose the **Finish Edit Mode** button from the **Mode** panel of the **Modify |
    Create Roof Footprint** tab; the **Revit** message box is displayed.

13. In the message box, choose the **Yes** button to attach the highlighted walls to the roof.

14. Next, to assign a type to the created roof, select the desired option from the **Type Selector** drop-down list in the **Properties** palette.

> For Imperial **Basic Roof : Insulation on Metal Deck - EPDM**
> For Metric **Basic Roof : Steel Bar Joist Steel Deck - EPDM Membrane**

15. Double-click on **North** from the **Elevations (Building Elevation)** head in the **Project Browser** to view the roof, refer to Figure 7-12. Make sure the **Shaded** option is chosen in the **View Control Bar**.

Figure 7-12 *North elevation of the Club project with the created roof*

In the following steps, you will create a flat roof for the **Lounge** area of the Club building.

16. Double-click on **Roof** in the **Floor Plans** head of the **Project Browser**.

17. Invoke the **Roof by Footprint** tool from **Architecture > Build > Roof** drop-down.

18. In the **Options Bar**, clear the **Defines slope** check box.

19. Ensure that the **Overhang** edit box shows **4'0"(1220 mm)** as the overhang value.

20. Choose the **Wireframe** option from the **Visual Style** menu of the **View Control Bar**.

21. Now, move the cursor near the curved wall of the Lounge area. Click when the dashed line appears on the outer face of the wall to sketch the roof boundary curve, as shown in Figure 7-13.

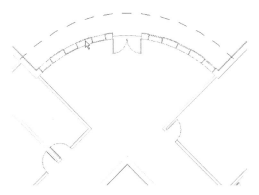

Figure 7-13 *Sketching the curved roof profile*

To sketch the other two lines for the Lounge roof, you need to use the **Line** tool from the **Draw** panel of the **Modify | Create Roof Footprint** tab.

22. Ensure that the **Boundary Line** tool is chosen in the **Draw** panel, and then choose the **Line** tool from the list box.

23. Clear the **Chain** check box in the **Options Bar**.

24. Ensure that the **Defines slope** check box in the **Options Bar** is cleared. Sketch the two lines to complete the boundary of the Lounge roof, as shown in Figure 7-14.

Figure 7-14 The completed roof profile of the Lounge

25. In the **Properties** palette, click on the value column for the **Base Level** instance parameter and ensure that the **Roof** option is selected from the drop-down list displayed.

26. Enter the value **-1'4" (-407 mm)** in the value column for the **Base Offset From Level** parameter as specified in the project parameter.

27. Choose the **Apply** button to apply the specified properties to the roof.

28. Next, choose the **Finish Edit Mode** button from the **Mode** panel of the **Modify | Create Roof Footprint** tab.
On choosing the **Finish Edit Mode** button; the **Revit** message box displays asking whether you would like to attach highlighted walls to the roof. Choose the **OK** button; the walls will be attached to the roof.

29. Next, you need to assign a type to the flat roof. Select the **Basic Roof : Insulation on Metal Deck-EPDM** (for imperial) option **Basic Roof : Steel Bar Joist-Steel Deck-EPDM Membrane** (for metric) from the **Type Selector** drop-down list in the **Properties** palette. Press **ESC** to exit from the **Floor: Architectural** tool.

Now, you need to create roof for Hall 2. Since the roof of Hall 2 is identical to the roof of Hall 1, you can use the **Mirror-Draw Axis** tool to mirror the roof of Hall 1 to create the roof of Hall 2.

30. Double-click on **Roof** in the **Floor Plans** head in the **Project Browser** to display the roof plan of the club building.

31. Before you use the **Mirror-Draw Axis** tool, you need to display the grids in the drawing. Choose the **Visibility/ Graphics** tool from the **Graphics** panel; the **Visibility/ Graphic Overrides for Floor Plan : Roof Framing** dialog box is displayed.

32. Choose the **Annotation Categories** tab, select the **Grids** check box if it is not selected in the **Visibility** column, and then choose **OK**; the **Visibility/Graphic Overrides for Floor Plan : Roof** dialog box is closed.

33. Now, select the roof of Hall 1; the **Modify | Roofs** tab is displayed.

34. Choose the **Mirror - Draw Axis** tool from the **Modify** panel; you are prompted to pick the start point for the axis of reflection.

35. Click at the point of intersection of the grids A2 and B2 to specify the start point for the axis.

36. Next, click at any point vertically up, as shown in Figure 7-15. Press ESC to exit the modification mode.

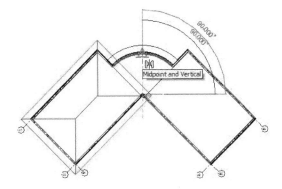

Figure 7-15 *Mirroring the roof of Hall 1*

37. Double-click on **North** in the **Elevations** node of the **Project Browser** to view the north elevation of the club building, as shown in Figure 7-16.

Figure 7-16 *North elevation of the Club project with the completed roof profile*

Attaching Walls to the Floor

While creating the roof, you have already attached the walls to its bottom. Now, you need to attach the walls to the floor using the **Attach** tool.

1. Double-click on **Section X** under the **Sections (Building Section)** head in this **Project Browser** to display the corresponding section view in the drawing window.

2. Move the cursor near the exterior wall, and when it is highlighted, press the TAB key; all the exterior walls get highlighted. Now, click to select the chain of exterior walls in the section view.

3. In the **Modify | Walls** tab, choose the **Attach Top/Base** tool from the **Modify Wall** panel; the options for attachment are displayed in the **Options Bar**.

4. Select the **Base** radio button in the **Options Bar**.

5. Next, move the cursor near the floor and click when it is highlighted; the walls get attached to the floor. Now, choose the **Modify** button from the **Select** panel to exit the modification tool.

    This completes the tutorial of creating floor, ceiling, and roof for the *Club* project.

6. Double-click on **First Floor** in the **Floor Plans** head of the **Project Browser** to display the first floor plan in the drawing window.

Saving the Project

In this section, you will save the project file using the **Save As** tool.

1. Choose **Save As > Project** from **the File** menu; the **Save As** dialog box is displayed. Enter required name in the **File name** edit box
    For Imperial   **c07_Club_tut2**
    For Metric   **M_c07_Club_tut2**
    Choose **Save**; the project file is saved.

2. Choose **Close** from the **File** menu to close the file.

EXERCISES

Exercise 1   Apartment 2

Create a floor and a ceiling on the First Floor level of the *c06_Apartment2_ex1.rvt* (*M_c06_Apartment2_ex1.rvt* for Metric) project created in Exercise 1 of Chapter 6. Attach the walls to the floor. Use the following project parameters: **(Expected time: 30 min)**

1. Floor type -
    For Imperial   **Floor: LW Concrete on Metal Deck**
    For Metric   **160mm Concrete With 50mm Metal Deck**
    Extents to wall core.

2. Ceiling type-
    For Imperial   **Compound Ceiling: GWB on Mtl Stud**
    For Metric   **Compound Ceiling: Plain**
    Level- 8'6" (2591 mm) from the First Floor level.

3. Name of the file to be saved-
    For Imperial   **c07_Apartment2_ex1**
    For Metric   **M_c07_Apartment2_ex1**

Exercise 2   Elevator and Stair Lobby

Create a floor and ceiling on the First Floor level of the *c06_ElevatorandStairLobby_ex2.rvt (M_ c06_ElevatorandStairLobby_ex2.rvt* for Metric*)* project created in Exercise 2 of Chapter 6. Attach the walls to the floor. Also, create openings in the floor and ceiling based on Figure 7-17. Use the following project parameters. Hide the grids and sections of the building and do not create the floor and ceiling in the elevator shafts.   **(Expected time: 30 min)**

1. Floor type -
    For Imperial   **LW Concrete on Metal Deck**
    For Metric   **160mm Concrete With 50mm Metal Deck**
    Extents to wall core.

2. Ceiling type-
    For Imperial   **GWB on Mtl Stud**
    For Metric   **Plain**
    Level- 8'6" (2591 mm) from the floor level.

3. Name of the file to be saved-
    For Imperial   **c07_ElevatorandStairLobby_ex2**
    For Metric   **M_c07_ElevatorandStairLobby_ex2**

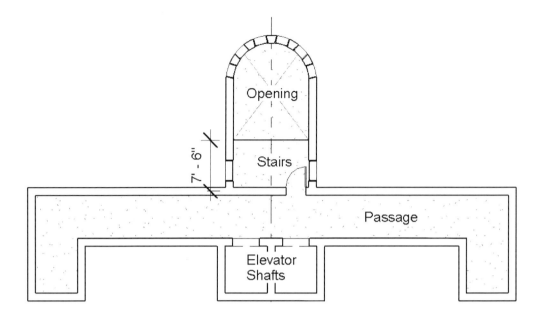

Figure 7-17 *Sketch plan for creating an opening for the Elevator and Stair Lobby project*

Chapter 8

Using Basic Building Components-III

Learning Objectives

After completing this chapter, you will be able to:

• *Add components to a building model*
• *Create stairs using the Stairs tool*
• *Understand the procedure of adding ramps to a building model*

USING COMPONENTS IN A PROJECT

Autodesk Revit provides various freestanding components that can be placed in a project. These include furniture items, plumbing fixtures, electrical fittings, trees, and many other family elements. Unlike other dependent elements, these freestanding components do not have any predefined associativity with other elements. However, it enables you to assign certain restrictions to their placement.

Adding Components

Ribbon:	Architecture > Build > Component drop-down > Place a Component
Shortcut Key:	CM

You can add components to a building model using the **Place a Component** tool. This tool can be invoked from the **Build** panel. On invoking this tool, the **Modify | Place Component** tab will be displayed. You can use the options in this tab to select the component type and specify the properties of the component to be inserted, load components from the predefined library, or create a new component in the drawing. Alternatively, type **CM** to invoke the **Place a Component** tool.

ADDING STAIRS

Ribbon:	Architecture > Circulation > Stair

In Autodesk Revit, you can create a variety of stair shapes such as straight, curved, and spiral stairs with ease. In Revit, stairs are parametric elements; therefore, you can create them by specifying the rules for risers, treads, and stringers. You can create stairs in your building design both in the plan and 3D views.

In Autodesk Revit, stairs can be added in individual components such as Run, Landing, and Supports. To do so, invoke the **Stair** tool from the **Circulation** panel; the **Modify|Create Stair** tab will be displayed. In the **Component** panel of this tab, you can choose the **Run**, **Landing**, or **Support** tool based on the requirement.

ADDING RAMPS

Ribbon:	Architecture > Circulation > Ramp

You can create ramps in Autodesk Revit in a manner similar to creating stairs. The **Ramp** tool is used to create ramps and can be invoked from the **Circulation** panel. On invoking this tool, the **Modify | Create Ramp Sketch** tab will be displayed. Also, the properties used for creating the ramp will be displayed in the **Properties** palette. You can use various tools and options in this tab to create the sketch of the ramp. In the **Properties** palette, you can assign properties and type to the ramp.

TUTORIALS

Tutorial 1 — Apartment 1

In this tutorial, you will add furniture and sanitary elements to the first floor level of the *c07_Apartment1_tut1.rvt* project created in Tutorial 1 of Chapter 7. The approximate location of components is shown in Figure 8-1. The text has been given for reference and is not to be created. Extend the exterior walls to 3'0" above the top floor level and copy all interior walls, doors, windows, and other elements at the same location on all three upper floors. Also, create a flat roof for the top floor. Use the following parameters for different components to be added:

(Expected time: 30 min)

Alphabets in Figure 8-1 represent the furniture and plumbing components to be used, as given below.

1. Furniture Components
   For Imperial: Furniture components from the **Furniture** folder of the **US Imperial**:
   - A- **Bed-Shaker: Double 56" x 78"**
   - B- **Entertainment Center-72" x 72" x 24"**
   - C- **Dresser-72" x 60" x 18"**
   - D- **Sofa-72"**
   - E- **Table-Dining Oval-36" x 72"**
   - F- **Table-Coffee-36" x 72"x 18"**
   - G- **Chair-Corbu**
   - H- **Table-End:24" x 24"** (modify height to 15")

   For Metric: Furniture components from the **Furniture** folder of the **US Metric**:
   - A- **Bed-Shaker: Double 1422 x 1981 mm**
   - B- **Entertainment Center- 1830 x 1830 x 610 mm**
   - C- **Dresser- 1220 x 1525 x 0610 mm**
   - D- **Sofa- 1830 mm**
   - E- **Table-Dining Oval- 0915 x 1830 mm**
   - F- **Table-Coffee- 0915 x 1830 x 0457 mm**
   - G- **Chair-Corbu**
   - H- **Table-End- 0610 x 0610 mm** (modify height to 381 mm)

2. Plumbing Components
   For Imperial: Plumbing components from **Speciality Equipment > Domestic** and **Plumbing** folders of **US Imperial**
   - J- **Kitchenette-Medium**: 8'6" (modified width)
   - K- **Toilet-Domestic-3D**
   - L- **Tub-Rectangular-3D**
   - M- **Sink Vanity-Square: 20" x 18"**

   For Metric: Plumbing components from **Speciality Equipment > Domestic** and **Plumbing** folders of **US Metric**
   - J- **Kitchenette-Medium**: 2591 mm (modified width)
   - K- **Toilet-Domestic-3D**
   - L- **Tub-Rectangular-3D**
   - M- **Sink Vanity-Square: 500 x 440 mm**

3. Top floor roof type-
    For Imperial   **Basic Roof : Generic 9"** - Flat
    For Metric   **Basic Roof : Generic 400 mm** - Flat

The following steps are required to complete this tutorial:

a. Open the project file, invoke the **Place a Component** tool, and load the components from the additional libraries using the **Load Family** tool.
b. Add and position the components at their desired location in the building model using the **Rotate** and **Move** tools, refer to Figures 8-2 and 8-3.
c. Extend the exterior walls to **3'0"(914 mm)** above the top most level, refer to Figure 8-4.
d. Select the doors, windows, floor, ceiling, and components, and copy them to all upper floors using the **Aligned to Selected Levels** tool, refer to Figure 8-5
e. Create the roof of the topmost floor using the **Roof** tool, refer to Figure 8-6.
f. Save the project using the **Save As** tool.
    For Imperial   *c08_Apartment1_tut1.rvt*
    For Metric   *M_c08_Apartment1_tut1.rvt*
g. Close the project.

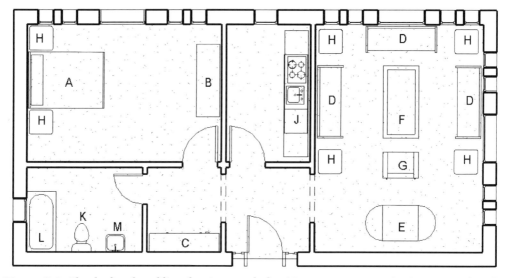

Figure 8-1 *Sketch plan for adding furniture and plumbing components to the Apartment 1 project*

Opening the Project File and Loading Components from Additional Libraries

In this section of the tutorial, you will first open the specified project file and add the components to the first floor plan view by using the **Component** tool. You will use the **Load Family** tool to load the components from the specified additional libraries.

1. Choose **Open > Project** from the **File** menu and open the *c07_Apartment1_tut1.rvt* file created in Tutorial 1 of Chapter 7 and make sure that the first floor plan is displayed. You can also download this file from *http://www.cadsofttech.com*. The path of the file is as follows: *Textbooks > Civil/GIS > Revit Architecture > Revit Architecture 2019 for Novices*.

2. Next, you need to place the components as specified in the project parameters. To do so, invoke the **Place a Component** tool from **Architecture > Build > Component** drop-down; the **Modify | Place Component** tab is displayed.

3. Next, you need to load additional components to the drawing. To do so, choose the **Load Family** tool from the **Mode** panel; the **Load Family** dialog box is displayed.

4. In the **Load Family** dialog box, select the desired folder to open it.
    For Imperial   **US Imperial > Furniture**
    For Metric   **US Metric > Furniture**

5. In this folder, select the following furniture types from their corresponding folders and load them one by one by repeating the procedure followed in steps 6 and 7.
    For Imperial: **Bed-Shaker** (Folder: Beds), **Chair-Corbu** (Folder: Seating), **Dresser** (Folder: Storage), **Entertainment Center** (Folder: Storage), **Sofa** (Folder: Seating), **Table-Dining Oval** (Folder: Tables), **Table-Coffee** (Folder: Tables), and **Table-End** (Folder: Tables).
    For Metric: **M_Bed-Shaker** (Folder: Beds), **M_Chair-Corbu** (Folder: Seating), **M_Dresser** (Folder: Storage), **M_Entertainment Center** (Folder: Storage), **M_Sofa** (Folder: Seating), **M_Table-Dining Oval** (Folder: Tables), **M_Table-Coffee** (Folder: Tables), and **M_Table-End** (Folder: Tables).

6. After selecting the required family, choose the **Open** button; the **Load Family** dialog box is closed and the selected type becomes available in the **Type Selector** drop-down list in the **Properties** palette. At this stage, it is recommended that you do not click in the drawing area or press ESC.

7. Invoke the **Load Family** dialog box. In this dialog box, choose the **Fixtures** folder from **US Imperial > Plumbing > Architectural** folder (For Metric, **US Metric > Plumbing > Architectural** folder). In the **Fixture** folder, load the following fixture types from their corresponding folders:

    For Imperial: **Sink Vanity- Square** (Folder: Sinks), **Toilet-Domestic-3D** (Folder: Water Closets), and **Tub-Rectangular-3D** (Folder: Bathtubs).

    For Metric: **M_Sink Vanity- Square** (Folder: Sinks), **M_Toilet-Domestic-3D** (Folder: Water Closets), and **M_Tub-Rectangular-3D** (Folder: Bathtubs).

8. Repeat step 3 to invoke the **Load Family** dialog box. In this dialog box, access the **Domestic** folder from **US Imperial > Speciality Equipment** (for Metric: **US Metric > Speciality Equipment**) and load **Kitchenette-Medium** (for Metric **M_Kitchenette-Medium**) into the project file.

Adding and Positioning Components in the Building Model

You can now select the component type from the **Type Selector** drop-down list and add it to the building model. Different editing tools like **Rotate**, **Copy**, and **Move** can be used to position the components at their desired location and in the required direction. The steps below describe the procedure for a single component, **Bed-Shaker**. The following steps can then be used to add and position other furniture and plumbing components. As mentioned earlier, the exact location of the components is not important for this tutorial.

1. In the **Type Selector** drop-down list of the **Properties** palette, select the **Bed-Shaker : Double 56" x 78"** (**Bed-Shaker : Double 1422 x 1981 mm** for metric) option, as specified in the parameters for the project.

2. Select the **Rotate after placement** check box in the **Options Bar**.

3. Move the cursor near the west wall of the bedroom and click at the desired location, as shown in Figure 8-2; the component is temporarily placed and the **Rotate** tool is invoked, as shown in Figure 8-3.

4. Move the cursor vertically upward and click when the dashed rectangle (indicating the direction of the bed) is horizontally positioned, as shown in Figure 8-3; the bed is added. Now, press ESC twice. Depending on the point selected for the placement, you may need to use the **Move** tool to move the component to the desired position.

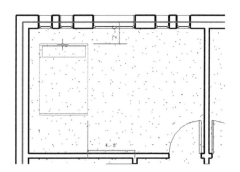

Figure 8-2   *Placing a component temporarily*

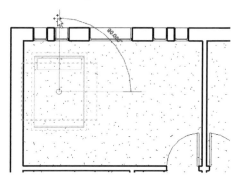

Figure 8-3   *Rotating the component*

5. Repeat steps 1 to 4 for adding and positioning the components in the building model at locations based on the given sketch plan, refer to Figure 8-1. The components are listed next according to their placements in sketch plan.
   For Imperial: **Entertainment Center : 72"x 72" x 24"**
   Dresser : 72" x 60" x 18"
   Sofa : 72"
   Table-Dining Oval : 36" x 72"
   Table-Coffee : 36" x 72" x 18"
   Chair-Corbu
   Table- End : 24" x 24"

Kitchenette - Medium : Kitchenette - Medium
Toilet-Domestic-3D
Tub-Rectangular-3D
Sink Vanity-Square : 20" x 18"

For Metric: **Entertainment Center : 1830 x 1830 x 610 mm**
Dresser : 1220 x 1525 x 0610 mm
Sofa : 1830 mm
Table-Dining Oval : 0915 x 1830 mm
Table-Coffee : 0915 x 1830 x 0457 mm
Chair-Corbu
Table- End : 0610 x 0610 mm
Kitchenette - Medium : Kitchenette - Medium
Toilet-Domestic-3D
Tub-Rectangular-3D
Sink Vanity-Square : 0500 x 0440 mm

6. After adding all components, press ESC twice.

Tip
On the basis of dimensions, you can place the components from the neighboring elements. To do so, select the component to display its temporary dimensions. Select the appropriate temporary dimension and enter the new value. The component is moved to the exact location.

Modifying the Added Components

The width of the **Kitchenette - Medium** and the height of the **Table- End : 24" x 24"** components can be modified by using the **Type Properties** dialog box.

1. Select the **Kitchenette-Medium : Kitchenette - Medium** component placed in the building model; the **Modify | Specialty Equipment** tab is displayed.

2. Choose the **Edit Type** button from the **Properties** palette; the **Type Properties** dialog box is displayed.

Note
*Create a new type for the **Kitchenette-Medium : Kitchenette - Medium** component if it already does not exist.*

3. In the **Type Properties** dialog box, choose the **Duplicate** button; the **Name** dialog box is displayed.

4. Enter **8'6" (2591 mm)** in the **Name** edit box and choose the **OK** button to close it.

5. In the **Type Properties** dialog box, enter **8'6" (2591 mm)** as the value for the **Cabinet Width** type parameter.

6. Choose the **OK** button to close this dialog box. The **Kitchenette - Medium** component is modified to the new size. You may need to use the **Move** tool to reposition the component at the desired location.

7. Similarly, select all the **Table-End : 24" x 24"** (for Metric **Table- End : 0610 x 0610 mm**) component, access the **Type Properties** dialog box, and then modify the value of the **Height** parameter to **1'3" (381 mm)**. This modifies the height of all instances of the component.

8. Choose the **OK** button; the **Type Properties** dialog box is closed.

    The first floor plan after adding and positioning the components should appear similar to the sketch plan given for this tutorial.

Extending Walls to the Topmost Level

As described earlier, it is better to extend the exterior walls to the top story, instead of stacking them one above the other. To extend the exterior wall height, you need to set the **Top Constraint** parameter to the topmost level and then use the 3D view to view the changes.

1. To change the current view to a 3D view, double-click on **3D** under the **3D Views** head in the **Project Browser**.
2. Now, move the cursor near the exterior wall and press the TAB key; the chain of exterior walls is highlighted.

3. Click to select the exterior walls; the **Modify | Walls** tab is displayed.

4. In the **Properties** palette for the **Top Constraint** instance parameter, select the **Up to level: Roof** option.

5. Replace the current value of the **Top Offset** parameter with **3'0" (915 mm)** as specified in the project parameters.

6. Choose the **Apply** button in the **Properties** palette. The exterior walls are extended to 3'0" (915mm) above the roof level, as shown in Figure 8-4. Press ESC to exit the tool.

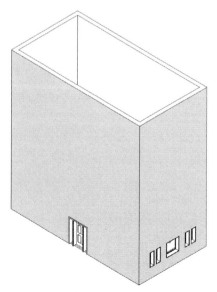

Figure 8-4   *Extending the exterior walls to the topmost level*

Copying Elements to Upper Levels

You can now select all elements except the exterior walls and use the **Aligned to Selected Levels** tool to copy them to the upper levels. The following steps describe the general procedure for copying elements to different levels by using the **Aligned to Selected Levels** tool.

1. In the 3D view, select all elements except the exterior walls and levels by creating a selection window from the left to right. All elements, including the interior walls, floor, ceiling, doors, windows, and components need to be selected.

Note

To exclude the exterior walls and levels, select all elements first and then press the SHIFT key and select the exterior walls and levels.

2. Choose the **Copy to Clipboard** tool from the **Clipboard** panel of the **Modify | Multi-Select** tab.

3. Now, choose the **Aligned to Selected Levels** tool from the **Modify | Multi-Select > Clipboard > Paste** drop-down; the **Select Levels** dialog box is displayed.

4. In this dialog box, select the **Second Floor, Third Floor**, and **Fourth Floor** levels by pressing and holding the CTRL button, as shown in Figure 8-5.

5. Choose the **OK** button to close the **Select Levels** dialog box. The selected elements and components are pasted on the three upper levels.

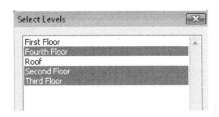

Figure 8-5 Specifying levels to paste the selected elements

Adding Roof to the Top Floor

The top floor is still without a roof. Therefore, you need to use the **Roof** tool to create a flat roof. It is recommended that you create the roof in its corresponding floor plan.

1. Double-click on **Roof** from the **Floor Plans** head in the **Project Browser** to display the roof plan.

2. Choose the **Roof by Footprint** tool from **Architecture > Build > Roof** drop-down; the **Modify | Create Roof Footprint** contextual tab is displayed.

3. Choose the **Pick Walls** tool from the **Draw** panel, if not chosen by default, and then clear the **Defines slope** check box in the **Options Bar**, if selected.

4. Move the cursor near the exterior wall of the plan, and when it is highlighted, press the TAB key to highlight the chain of exterior walls. Click to select them. The roof boundary is displayed. Ensure that it is displayed on the inner face. If it is not displayed on the inner face, click on the flip arrow to flip the selection.

5. Choose the **Finish Edit Mode** button from the **Mode** panel to create the roof boundary at the roof plan level.

6. Next, select the **Basic Roof : Generic - 9"** option (for Metric **Basic Roof : Generic - 400 mm**) from the **Type Selector** drop-down list in the **Properties** palette, as specified in the project parameters.

7. Double-click on **3D** under the **3D Views** head in the **Project Browser** to display the 3D view of the multistory apartment. You can use the **ViewCube** tool from the drawing window to view the other sides of the building model, as shown in Figure 8-6.

8. Double-click on **First Floor** from the **Floor Plans** head in the **Project Browser** to return to the first floor plan.

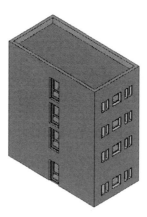

Figure 8-6 Completed multistory apartment

Saving the Project

In this section, you will save the project file using the **Save As** tool.

1. Choose **Save As > Project** from the **File** menu and enter the desired name in the **File name** edit box of the **Save As** dialog box.

    For Imperial   **c08_Apartment1_tut1**
    For Metric   **M_c08_Apartment1_tut1**

    Next, choose **Save**; the project file is saved.

2. Choose **Close** from the **File** menu to close the project file.

Tutorial 2 Club

In this tutorial, you will modify the two walls of the *Club* project created in Tutorial 2 of Chapter 7 into curtain walls and add mullions to all curtain grids. Figure 8-7 shows the walls that are to be modified. Use the parameters given next for the different components to be added.

(Expected time: 30 min)

1. Curtain wall type - **Curtain Wall: Exterior Glazing**
    Curtain grid spacing:
    For Imperial   Horizontal- **5'0"**, Vertical- **5'0"**
    For Metric   Horizontal- **1524 mm**, Vertical- **1524 mm**
2. Mullion type
    For Imperial   **Rectangular Mullion: 1.5" x 2.5" Rectangular**
    For Metric   **Rectangular Mullion: x 2.5" Rectangular**

The following steps are required to complete this tutorial:

a. Open the *c07_Club_tut2.rvt* project file created in Tutorial 2 of Chapter 7.
b. Select the walls and modify them into curtain walls using the **Type Selector** drop-down list.
c. Modify the vertical and horizontal spacing for curtain grids.
d. Add mullions using the **Mullion** tool, refer to Figures 8-8 and 8-9.
e. Save the project using the **Save As** tool.
    For Imperial   *c08_Club_tut2.rvt*
    For Metric   *M_c08_Club_tut2.rvt*
f. Close the project.

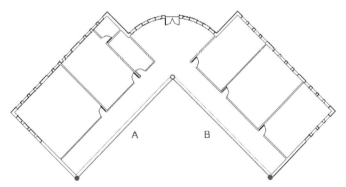

Figure 8-7 *Sketch plan for modifying the existing walls into curtain walls for the Club project*

Opening the Project File and Modifying the Wall Type

To modify the walls into curtain walls, first you need to open the *c07_Club_tut2.rvt* project file and then make sure that the **First Floor** plan is the current view.

1. Choose **Open > Project** from the **File** menu and open the *c07_Club_tut2.rvt* file, created in Tutorial 2 of Chapter 7. Also, open the first floor plan using the **Project Browser**. You can also download this file from *http://www.cadsofttech.com*. The path of the file is as follows: *Textbooks > Civil/GIS > Revit Architecture> Revit Architecture 2019 for Novices.*

2. Select the two walls marked A and B using the CTRL key, refer to the sketch plan; the **Modify | Walls** tab is displayed.

3. In the **Properties** palette, select the **Curtain Wall: Exterior Glazing** option from the **Type Selector** drop-down list. Autodesk Revit displays an error message indicating that the curtain wall cannot be joined to the exterior wall. Choose the **Unjoin Elements** button to proceed. The walls are replaced by the selected curtain wall type.

Modifying the Curtain Wall Parameters

Next, you will modify the vertical and horizontal spacing of the curtain grid using the **Type Properties** dialog box based on the given project parameters.

1. Ensure that the curtain walls are still selected. Next, choose the **Edit Type** button from the **Properties** palette; the **Type Properties** dialog box is displayed.

2. In the **Value** columns of the **Spacing** type parameter in the **Vertical Grid** pattern and **Horizontal Grid** pattern heads, enter the value **5'0"(1524 mm)**.

3. Choose the **Apply** and then **OK** button to return to the drawing window. The curtain wall grid is modified to the new spacing.

Modifying Curtain System Panels

Now, you need to replace the top row of the curtain wall panel with solid panels to hide the ceiling.

1. Open the **South** elevation using the **Project Browser**.

2. Select the top row of curtain panels using the crossing window; the **Modify | Curtain Panels** tab or the **Modify | Multi-Select** tab is displayed.

3. If the **Modify | Multi-Select** tab is displayed, choose the **Filter** tool from the **Selection** panel; the **Filter** dialog box is displayed.

4. In the **Filter** dialog box, clear all check boxes except the **Curtain Panels** check box and then choose the **OK** button to close the dialog box; the **Modify | Curtain Panels** tab is displayed.

5. In the **Properties** palette, select **System Panel : Solid** from the **Type Selector** drop-down list to replace the selected panels. Press ESC to exit.

Adding Mullions

Mullions can be added using the **Mullion** tool. You need to choose the **All Grid Lines** option to add mullions to all curtain grids.

1. Choose the **Mullion** tool from the **Build** panel of the **Architecture** tab; the **Modify | Place Mullion** tab is displayed.

2. In the **Properties** palette, select the desired mullion type from the **Type Selector** drop-down list.

> For Imperial **Rectangular Mullion: 1.5" x 2.5"**
> For Metric **Rectangular Mullion: 50 x 150 mm**

3. Choose the **All Grid Lines** tool from the **Placement** panel.

4. Move the cursor in the left curtain grid area and click when the curtain wall of Hall 1 is highlighted, as shown in Figure 8-8; the mullions are automatically added to all the curtain grids. Similarly, add mullions to the Hall 2 curtain walls. Choose the **Modify** tool from the **Select** panel of the **Modify| Place Mullion** contextual tab to exit the tool.

5. Choose the **Visual Style** button from the **View Control Bar** and choose the **Shaded** option from the flyout displayed to view the shaded South elevation, as shown in Figure 8-9.

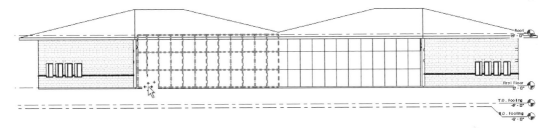

Figure 8-8 *Selecting a curtain wall to add mullions*

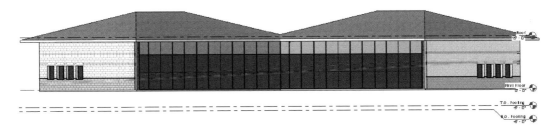

Figure 8-9 *South elevation of the club project showing the curtain wall created with mullions*

6. Double-click on the **First Floor** in the **Floor Plans** head in the **Project Browser** to return to the first floor plan view.

Saving the Project

In this section, you will save the project file using the **Save As** tool.

1. Choose **Save As > Project** from the **File** menu and enter the required name in the **File name** edit box of the **Save As** dialog box.

For Imperial	**c08_Club_tut2**
For Metric	**M_c08_Club_tut2**

    Next, choose **Save**; the project file is saved.

2. Choose **Close** from the **File** menu to close the file.

EXERCISES

Exercise 1	Apartment 2

Add furniture and sanitary components to the *c07_Apartment2_ex1.rvt* project created in Exercise 1 of Chapter 7. The approximate location of the components is given in Figure 8-10. The text has been given only for reference and is not to be created. Extend the exterior walls to 3'0" above the roof level and copy all interior walls, interior doors, windows, and components at the same location on all the three upper floors. Also, create a flat roof at the roof level. Use the following parameters for various components to be added. The Northeast 3D view of the completed project should appear similar to the illustration shown in Figure 8-11.

(Expected time: 30 min)

Alphabets in Figure 8-11 represent the furniture and plumbing components to be used, as given below.

1. Furniture Components

    For Imperial: Furniture components from the **Furniture** folder of the **US Imperial**:
    - A- **Bed Shaker: Double 56" x 78"**
    - B- **Entertainment Center: 72" x 72" x 24"**
    - C- **Dresser- 72" x 60" x 18"**
    - D- **Sofa: 72"**
    - E- **Table-Ellipse : 72" x 36"**
    - F- **Table-Coffee : 36" x 72" x 18"**
    - G- **Table-End: 24" x 24"**

    For Metric: Furniture components from the **Furniture** folder of the **US Metric**:
    - A- **Bed Shaker: Double 1422 x 1981 mm**
    - B- **Entertainment Center: 1830 x 1830 x 0610 mm**
    - C- **Dresser- 1220 x 1525 x 0610 mm**
    - D- **Sofa: 1830 mm**
    - E- **Table-Ellipse : 1800 x 0900 mm**
    - F- **Table-Coffee : 0915 x 1830 x 457 mm**
    - G- **Table-End: 0610 x 0610 mm**

2. Plumbing Components

   For Imperial: Plumbing components from the **Plumbing Fixtures** folder of the **US Imperial**:
   J- **Kitchenette-Medium**: **8'6"** (modified size)
   K- **Toilet-Domestic-3D**
   L- **Tub-Rectangular-3D**
   M- **Sink Vanity- Square: 24" x 19"**

   For Metric: Plumbing components from the **Plumbing Fixtures** folder of the **US Metric**:
   J- **Kitchenette-Medium**: **2591 mm** (modified size)
   K- **Toilet-Domestic-3D**
   L- **Tub-Rectangular-3D**
   M- **Sink Vanity- Square 0610 x 0483 mm**

3. Roof type- **Basic Roof: Generic 400mm** - Flat.

4. Name of the file to be saved-

   > **For Imperial**   c08_Apartment2_ex1
   > **For Metric**   M_c08_Apartment2_ex1

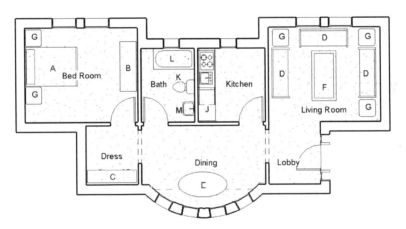

Figure 8-10 *Sketch plan for adding components to the Apartment 2 project*

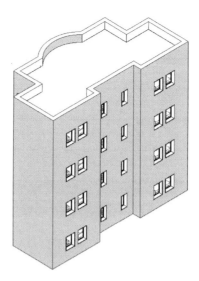

Figure 8-11 *The Northeast 3D view of the Apartment 2 project*

Chapter 9

Adding Site Features

Learning Objectives

After completing this chapter, you will be able to:
- *Create contoured sites using the Toposurface tool*
- *Add property lines to the site plan using the Property Line tool*
- *Add building pads in the site plan using the Building Pad tool*
- *Add site components and plantations to the site plan*

WORKING WITH SITE FEATURES

Autodesk Revit provides you with various tools to create site features. These tools can be accessed from the **Model Site** and **Modify Site** panels in the **Massing & Site** tab, refer to Figure 9-1.

*Figure 9-1 Tools in the **Massing & Site** tab*

Tip
You can also generate a toposurface by picking points at different elevations. To do so, first pick points at one elevation, change the elevation, and then pick points at the new elevation.

Creating a Toposurface

Ribbon: Massing & Site > Model Site > Toposurface

A toposurface, also called topographical surface, is a graphical representation of the terrain of the site of a building project. The topograhical surfaces comprises of contour lines to represent elevation of the terrain. To create a toposurface for a building project, invoke the **Site** floor plan view or a **{3D}** view from the **Project Browser** and then invoke the **Toposurface** tool from the **Model Site** panel. On doing so, the **Modify | Edit Surface** tab will be displayed. The tools displayed in this tab are shown in Figure 9-2. They can be used to sketch and create topographical surfaces which are defined by picking the elevation points.

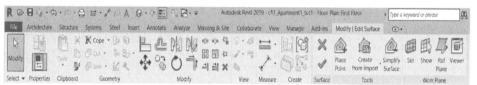

*Figure 9-2 Tools displayed in the **Modify / Edit Surface** tab*

ADDING PROPERTY LINES

Ribbon: Massing & Site > Modify Site > Property Line

The **Property Line** tool is used to demarcate and define the extents of the property of a building project based on the survey data. Property lines can be sketched only in the plan views; therefore, these lines can be created only when a plan view, preferably a site plan view, is selected. Property lines can be added by two methods. The first method is by entering distances and bearings and the second method is by sketching. On invoking the **Property Line** tool from the **Massing & Site** tab, the **Create Property Line** window will be displayed, as shown in Figure 9-3.

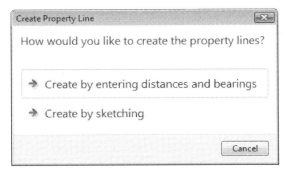

*Figure 9-3 The **Create Property Line** window showing the methods for creating the property line*

Creating Building Pads

Ribbon: Massing & Site > Model Site > Building Pad

In a project, you can develop a level area for your building model in the site. This level area, which provides a minimal slope for a building drainage, is called a building pad. The creation of a building pad provides you more flexibility in the design as you will not be dictated by grade elevations, floor transitions, building shapes or other consideration. In Revit, you can create a building pad by using the **Building Pad** tool. To do so, invoke this tool from the **Model Site** panel of the **Massing & Site** tab; the **Modify | Create Pad Boundary** tab will be displayed.

Note
*The building pad is a toposurface hosted element and can be added only to an existing topographical surface. This **Building Pad** tool will be activated in the **Model Site** panel only if there is an existing toposurface in the drawing.*

ADDING SITE COMPONENTS

Ribbon: Massing & Site > Model Site > Site Component

You can add different site components such as trees, bollards, building signs, planters, and so on to a site using the **Site Component** tool. The procedure for adding site components is similar to that of adding building components (for more information, refer to the Adding Components section in Chapter 8).

Invoke the **Site Component** tool from the **Model Site** panel in the **Massing & Site** tab; the **Modify | Site Component** tab will be displayed. In the **Properties** palette, select the component to be added from the **Type Selector** drop-down list and insert it into the drawing. You can add other components in your drawing apart from those available in the **Type Selector** drop-down list. To do so, choose the **Load Family** button in the **Mode** panel of the **Modify | Site Component** tab; the **Load Family** dialog box will be displayed. You can use this dialog box to load site components from the libraries available in the **US Imperial > Site** folder location. This folder contains four subfolders: **Accessories**, **Logistics**, **Parking**, and **Utilities**. Each subfolder contains elements related to its title. For example, the **Utilities** subfolder contains elements such as **Fire Hydrant**, **Manhole**, and so on.

After choosing the desired components from the **Load Family** dialog box, choose the **OK** button; the components chosen will be added to the **Type Selector** drop-down list in the **Properties** palette. Now, you can choose the appropriate component type to add it to the site.

To add planting components to the site, load the plantation elements from the **Planting** subfolder in the **US Imperial** folder using the **Load Family** dialog box. Next, select the tree type from the **Type Selector** drop-down list and add it to the site in the site plan view, as shown in Figure 9-4.

After you add trees to the site, they automatically get attached to the topographical level at the specified point of placement. The added components can be viewed in the section or 3D view of the site. The trees appear as simple lines unless the view is rendered. Figure 9-5 shows a rendered view of the contoured site with trees.

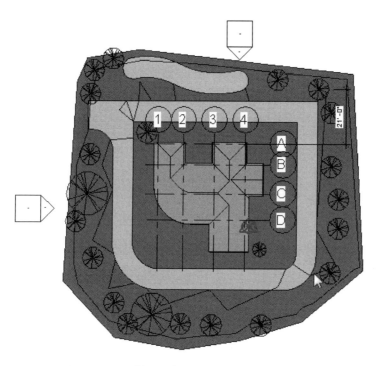

Figure 9-4 *Adding planting components to a contoured site*

Figure 9-5 *Rendered view of the contoured sites with trees*

TUTORIAL

Tutorial 1   Site Plan

In this tutorial, you will create a contoured site plan for an apartment complex on the basis of Figure 9-6. The approximate locations and sizes of roads, parking components, building pads and site components are also given. You can assume the missing dimensions. The texts and dimensions have been given only for reference and are not to be created. Given below are the parameters for various components to be added.

(Expected time: 2hr 15 min)

1. Project file parameters:
    Template file-
      For Imperial ***default.rte***
      For Metric ***DefaultMetric.rte***

    File name to be assigned-
      For Imperial *c09_SitePlan_tut1.rvt*
      For Metric *M_c09_SitePlan_tut1.rvt*

2. Property size:
      For Imperial **600'0" X 500'0"** (Extents of property line)
      For Metric 180000 X 15000 mm

3. Site settings:
    Contours at **1'0"(300 mm)** intervals
    Site material- **Grass**, Road material- **Asphalt**

Elevation of Poche base-
For Imperial   **5'0"**
For Metric   **1500 mm**

4. Building pads:
    Apartment blocks-3 Nos. building pads- size **106'0" X 151'0" (31800 X 45300 mm)** - placed symmetrically about the center of the design scheme

    Club 1 and Club 2-symmetrical building pads as per the dimensions given in sketch plan
    Building pad level-Level 2

5. Width of the straight pedestrian walkway- **8'(2400 mm)**, circular- **12'(3600 mm)**.

6. Parking Component:
    For Imperial   **Parking Space: 9' X 18': 90 deg**
    For Metric   **Parking Space: 4800 X 2400 mm- 90 deg**

7. Site Component:
    For Imperial   **Tree - Deciduous: Red Ash - 25'** placed on Level 2.
    For Metric   **RPC Tree - Deciduous : Red Ash- 7.6 Metres**

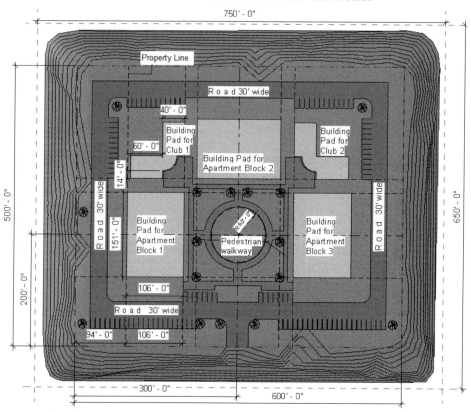

Figure 9-6 *Sketch plan for creating the site plan with contours, site components, and building pads*

The following steps are required to complete this tutorial:

a.   Open a new project file using the default template file and open the **Site Plan** view.
b.   Create reference planes to assist in sketching contours.
c.   Modify the site setting to create additional contours at **1'0"** interval.
d.   Use the **Topographies** tool to sketch the contours, refer to Figures 9-7 through 9-9.
e.   Create property line using reference planes and the **Property Line** tool, refer to Figure 9-10.
f.   Add building pads using the **Building Pad** tool, refer to Figures 9-11 through 9-13.
g.   Use the **Subregion** tool to create roads, refer to Figures 9-14 and 9-15.
h.   Add parking components using the **Parking Component** tool, refer to Figures 9-16 through 9-18.
i.   Add site components using the **Site Component** tool, refer to Figures 9-19 through 9-22.
j.   Save the project using the **Save As** tool.
      For Imperial   *c09_SitePlan_tut1.rvt*
      For Metric   *M_c09_SitePlan_tut1.rvt*
k.   Close the project.

Opening a New Project File and the Site Plan View

In this section, you will open a new project file using the **New** tool. As mentioned earlier, the site contours should be created in the **Site** view. Therefore, you will open the **Site** view using the **Project Browser**. You can also hide the elevation tags using the **Visibility/Graphics** tool.

1.   Choose the **New** option under the **Projects** head from the interface screen; the **New Project** dialog box is displayed.

2.   Choose the **Browse** button; the **Choose Template** dialog box is displayed.

3.   In the **Choose Template** dialog box, select the *default* template file from the **US Imperial** folder (For Metric select the *DefaultMetric* template file from the **US Metric** folder) and choose **Open**; the **New Project** dialog box is displayed. Next, choose the **OK** button; the dialog box closes and a new project file opens in the drawing window.

4.   In the **Project Browser**, double-click on **Site** under the head **Floor Plans** to display the site plan view.

5.   Select any elevation symbol in the drawing window and right-click; a shortcut menu is displayed.

6.   Choose **Hide in View > Category** from the shortcut menu; the elevation symbol hides in the site plan view. Similarly, select the project base point and the survey point symbols in the drawing window and then hide them.

Creating Reference Planes

Before creating contours, you need to draw reference planes to provide guidelines for sketching the site periphery and contour profile. In this section, you will draw the reference planes for the contour profile.

1. Invoke the **Ref Plane** tool from the **Work Plane** panel in the **Architecture** tab.

2. Move the cursor to the drawing window and click on the upper left corner of the screen to start creating the first reference plane.

3. Now, move the cursor horizontally to the upper right corner of the screen and click to end the reference plane.

4. Next, to create the second reference plane, move the cursor to the lower left corner of the drawing window in alignment with the first reference plane and then click at an appropriate location; the creation of the second reference plane starts.

5. Now, move the cursor horizontally to the lower right corner and click to end the second reference plane. Notice that a temporary dimension appears between the two reference planes.

6. Now, click on the value of the temporary dimension; an edit box is displayed. Enter **650'0"(198120 mm)** in the edit box and press ENTER.

7. Similarly, create two vertical reference planes at a distance of **750'0"** (**228600**).

8. Now, right-click on the open area of the drawing window; a shortcut menu is displayed. Choose the **Zoom To Fit** option from the shortcut menu; the screen view fits to the extent of the sketched reference plane, offering more clarity to the view displayed.

9. Press ESC twice to exit the **Ref Plane** tool.

10. Now, use the dragging method to extend the four reference planes, horizontally and vertically, such that they intersect each other, as shown in the sketch plan in Figure 9-6.

Modifying the Site Settings

Before creating the contours, you need to modify the site settings to achieve the desired contour layout. In this section, you will use the **Site Settings** dialog box to set parameters for creating additional contours. Then, you will create three topographical surfaces to generate all site contours, as shown in the sketch plan.

1. Choose the **Massing & Site** tab and then choose the inclined arrow button placed on the right of the **Model Site** panel; the **Site Settings** dialog box is displayed.

2. Make sure that the check box that is placed before the **At Intervals of** edit box is selected and then enter **1'0" (304.8 mm)** in the **At Intervals of** edit box. Also, ensure that in the **Passing Through Elevation** edit box 0' 0" (0) is entered.

3. Now, in the **Site Settings** dialog box, choose the **Insert** button to insert additional contours.

4. In the **Increment** column of the **Additional Contours** table, ensure that for Imperial **1' 0"** and for Metric **1000** is set as the default value.

5. In the **Section Graphics** area, choose the browse button under the **Section cut material** edit box; the **Material Browser** dialog box is displayed. In this dialog box, enter **Grass** as the material in the **Searches for Material** edit box and press ENTER; the Grass material is displayed in the Autodesk Material Library.

 Note

*If the Autodesk Library panel is not displayed, then choose the **Shows/Hides library panel** button from the right side of the **Project Materials: All** pane.*

6. Double-click on Grass in **Autodesk Material Library**, it is added under the **Project Materials: All** area.

7. Select the material under the **Project Materials: All** area and choose **OK** to accept the other specified values and to close the **Material Browser** dialog box.

8. In the **Section Graphics** area of the **Site Settings** dialog box, enter **-5'0" (-1525 mm)** in the **Elevation of poche base** edit box.

9. Now, choose **OK**; the specified setting is applied and the **Site Settings** dialog box is closed.

Creating Site Contours

In this section, you will use the **Topographies** tool and the **Point** tool and also pick points to generate the desired profile of contours. The contours should be created from the lowest to the highest level to be fully visible. You can first create a topographical surface at the base level and then create two more surfaces at **5'0"(1525 mm)** and **10'0"(3048 mm)** levels, respectively. On doing so, the Autodesk Revit automatically generates the intermediate contours at **1'0"** (304.8 mm) level.

1. Choose the **Toposurface** tool from the **Model Site** panel in the **Massing & Site** tab; the **Modify | Edit Surface** contextual tab is displayed. Ensure that the **Place Point** tool in the **Tools** panel is invoked, the **Elevation** edit box in the **Options Bar** shows **0'0"** as the elevation, and the **Absolute Elevation** option is selected (default option) in the drop-down list.

2. Move the cursor to the upper left corner and click to start the topographical surface. Ensure that the toposurface is drawn within the sketched reference plane.

   Click on multiple points to form a closed loop, as shown in Figure 9-7. The exact shape of the toposurface profile is not important for this tutorial.

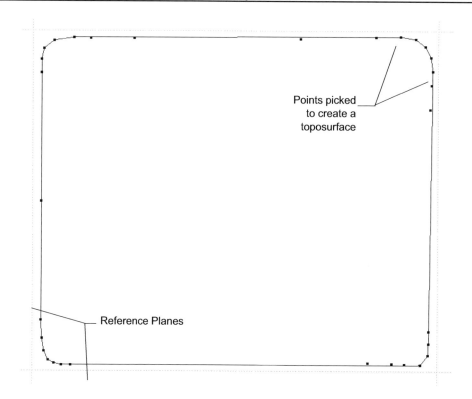

Points picked
to create a
toposurface

Reference Planes

Figure 9-7 Picking points to sketch the lowest topographical surface of the site plan

3. Choose the **Finish Surface** button from the **Surface** panel in the **Modify | Edit Surface** tab to complete the lowest topographical surface.

4. Select the toposurface created; the **Modify | Topography** tab is displayed. In this tab, choose the **Edit Surface** tool from the **Surface** panel; the **Modify | Edit Surface** tab is displayed.

5. Choose the **Place Point** tool from the **Tools** panel.

6. In the **Options Bar**, enter **5'0" (1525 mm)** in the **Elevation** edit box and press ENTER.

7. Next, move the cursor to the upper left corner of the toposurface created and click inside it to start the second topographical surface.

8. Click on multiple points along the inner surface of the first profile to create the second topographical surface, as shown in Figure 9-8. You will notice that as you pick the points, Autodesk Revit automatically generates the intermediate contours at **5'0"** level.

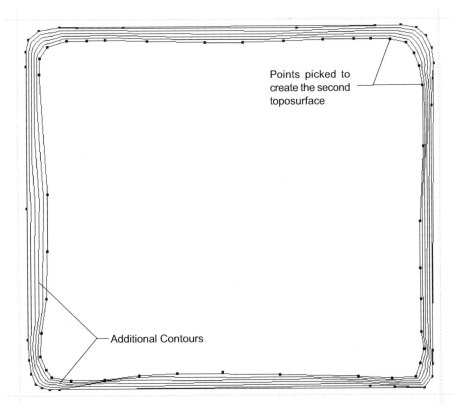

Points picked to
create the second
toposurface

Additional Contours

Figure 9-8 *Picking points to sketch the topographical surface at **5'0"** level*

9. Choose the **Finish Surface** button from the **Modify | Edit Surface** tab to create the second topographical surface.

10. Similarly, using the **Edit Surface** tool create the third topographical surface at **10'0"** (3048mm) level from the second toposurface, as shown in Figure 9-9.

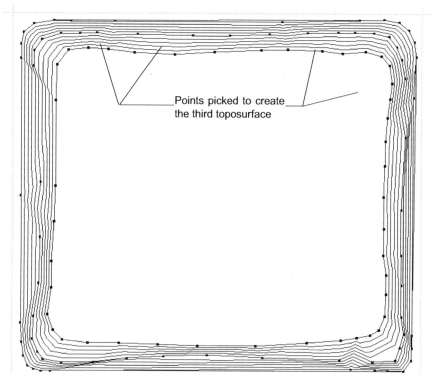

Points picked to create
the third toposurface

Figure 9-9 Picking points to sketch the third topographical surface at 10'0" level

11. After creating the toposurface, choose the **Finish Surface** tool from the **Surface** panel of
the **Modify|Edit Surface** tab.

Adding the Property Line

In this section, you will create a property line of an appropriate length using the **Property
Line** tool. You will create reference planes to locate the corner of the property line.

1. Choose the **Architecture** tab, and then invoke the **Ref Plane** tool from the **Work Plane**
panel. Now, you can start creating the desired reference planes.

2. Create two horizontal reference planes at a distance of **500' (152400 mm)** and two vertical
reference planes at a distance of **600' (182880 mm)**, intersecting at the four corners of the
property line, as specified in the sketch plan.

3. Choose the **Massing & Site** tab and then choose the **Property Line** tool from the **Modify
Site** panel; the **Create Property Line** window is displayed.

4. In this window, choose the **Create by sketching** option; the **Modify | Create Property Line
Sketch** tab is displayed.

5. From the **Draw** panel in the **Modify | Create Property Line Sketch** tab, choose the **Rectangle**
tool.

6. Now, sketch the rectangular property line by selecting the two diagonal intersections of the reference planes created in step 2. The temporary dimensions displayed can be used to verify the size of the sketched rectangle.

7. Choose the **Finish Edit Mode** button to finish sketching the property line. Figure 9-10 shows the property line created (highlighted for illustration purpose).

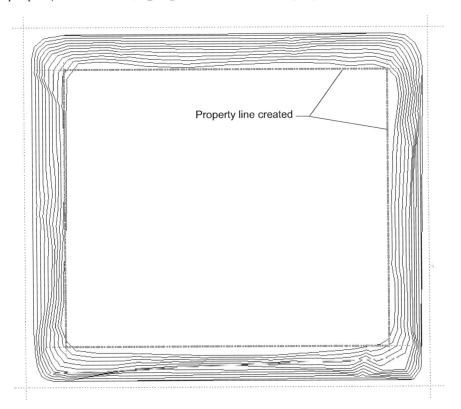

Property line created

Figure 9-10 Property line created for the site plan

Adding the Building Pads

The next step is to add building pads to the site plan. They are placed symmetrically around the central point of the layout. You will first create a single apartment block building pad and then use the **Radial Array** tool to create multiple copies of the building pad. The club-building pad can be added using the sketching tools. But, first you must locate the center of the design scheme using the reference planes.

1. Choose the **Architecture** tab and then choose the **Ref Plane** tool from the **Work Plane** panel.

2. Create a horizontal reference plane at a distance of **200'** (**60960 mm**) from the lower horizontal property line. Now, create a vertical reference plane between the midpoint of the two horizontal property lines, as given in the sketch plan. Their point of intersection is the center of the design scheme. Similarly, create additional reference planes to locate building pads which are shown in Figure 9-11.

3. Choose the **Massing & Site** tab and then choose the **Building Pad** tool from the **Model Site** panel; the **Modify | Create Pad Boundary** tab is displayed.

4. In the **Properties** palette, select the **Level 2** option from the drop-down list displayed in the value field of the **Level** instance parameter.

5. Ensure that the **Boundary Line** button is chosen in the **Draw** panel, and then invoke the **Rectangle** tool from the list box.

6. Sketch the Apartment Block 1 building pad with the dimension **106' X 151' (32308 x 46024 mm)** by clicking on the two diagonal intersection points on the reference planes, refer to sketch.

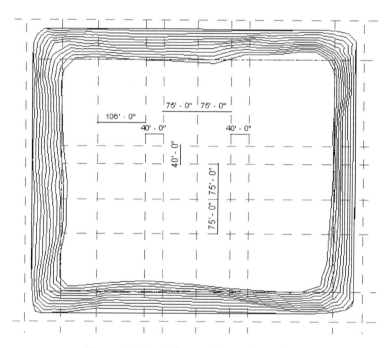

Figure 9-11   *Reference Plane dimensions*

7. Choose the **Finish Edit Mode** button from the **Mode** panel in the **Modify |Create Pad Boundary** tab to add the building pad, as shown in Figure 9-12; the **Modify|Pads** tab is displayed.

8. Select the created building pad, if not selected, to create its radial array and then choose the **Array** tool from the **Modify** panel in the **Modify | Pads** tab.

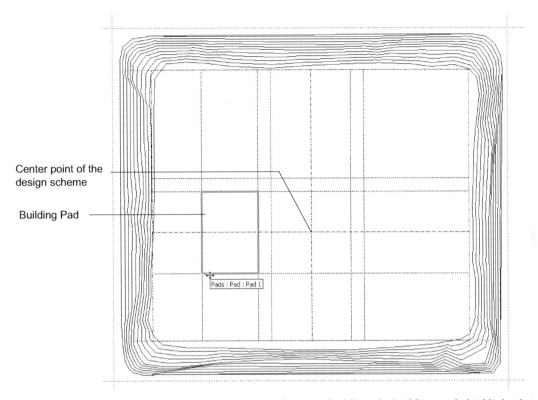

Figure 9-12 Creating reference planes and adding the building pad (highlighted)

9. Choose the **Radial** button from the **Options Bar** and then create the two additional building pads by moving the center of the radial array to the center of the design scheme, as shown in Figure 9-13.

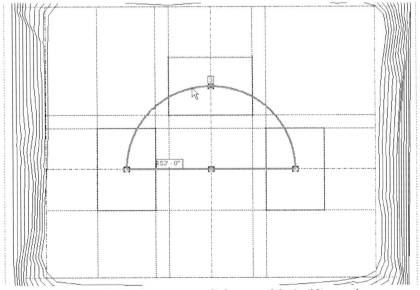

Figure 9-13 Creating a radial array of the building pad

10. Similarly, sketch the building pad for the club building based on the dimensions and location, refer to Figure 9-14. Use the **Mirror - Pick Axis** tool or the **Mirror-Draw Axis** tool to create a copy of this pad, as shown in Figure 9-14.

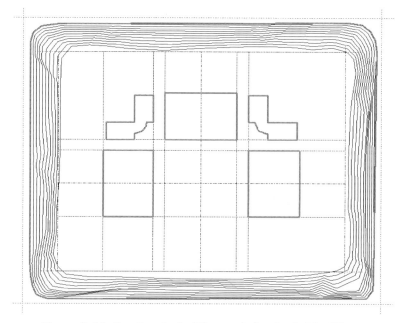

Figure 9-14 *Creating the building pads for the club buildings*

Creating Roads Using the Subregion Tool

Now, create roads for the site plan using the **Subregion** tool. You can create a subregion on the topographical surface in such a manner that a separate surface is created for the road. It can then be assigned a different material. You can use the sketching tools to sketch the road profile.

1. Before you create subregions for the road and the pedestrian walkway, the first thing you need to do is sketch the reference planes for them according to the dimensions and locations given in the sketch plan, refer to Figure 9-23. To do so, choose the **Architecture** tab and invoke the **Ref Plane** tool from the **Work Plane** panel to create reference planes to locate all corners of the outer profile of the road and the references for the pedestrian walkway.

2. Now, create a subregion for the road. To do so, choose the **Massing & Site** tab and then choose the **Subregion** tool from the **Modify Site** panel; the **Modify | Create Subregion Boundary** tab is displayed.

3. Next, use the sketching tools in the **Draw** panel to sketch the road profile according to the sketch plan.

4. After you sketch the road profile, choose the **Finish Edit Mode** button from the **Mode** panel; the topographical subregion is created and displayed, as shown in Figure 9-15 (highlighted for illustration purpose).

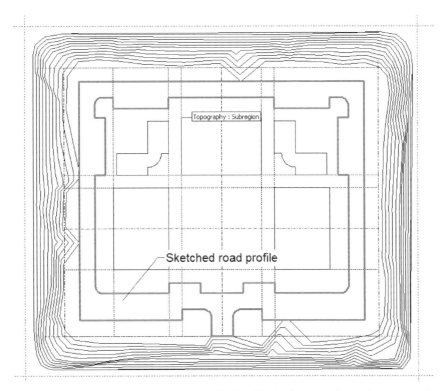

*Figure 9-15 Creating the road profile (highlighted) using the **Subregion** tool*

5. Similarly, create another subregion for the pedestrian walkway to enter each apartment block, as shown in Figure 9-16, by using the available sketching and editing tools.

    After creating contours, building pads, and subregions, you need to assign the appropriate material to their surface. This tutorial introduces you to the concept of applying materials to various elements. You will learn more about using materials in Chapter 15.

6. To apply a material to the road subregion, select it; the instance properties of the selected subregion are displayed in the **Properties** palette.

7. In this palette, click on the value field for the **Material** instance parameter and then choose the **Browse** button on the right of the edit box to display the **Material Browser** dialog box.

8. From the list of names, select **Asphalt Shingle** and then choose the **OK** button; the **Material Browser** dialog box is closed.

9. Similarly, select the site contours toposurface and apply the material **Grass** to it.

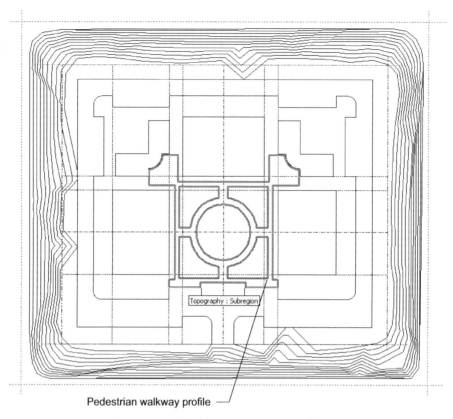

Pedestrian walkway profile

Figure 9-16 Pedestrian walkway profile created

Adding Parking Components

In this section, you will add the parking components to the site plan using the **Parking Component** tool.

1. Choose the **Massing & Site** tab and then choose the **Parking Component** tool from the **Model Site** panel; the **Modify | Parking Component** tab is displayed.

2. In the **Properties** palette, select the **Parking Space: 9' X 18'-90 deg (4800 X 2400 mm- 90 deg)** option from the **Type Selector** drop-down list, as specified in the component parameters for the project.

3. Move the cursor near the entrance of the lower left corner of the site and click near the location shown in Figure 9-17. (You may need to use the **Zoom In Region** tool to enlarge the portion of the site). The selected parking component is added to the site plan. Depending upon the point selected for placement, you may need to use the **Move** or **Flip** tool to orient the component to the desired position.

4. Create multiple copies of the added parking component using the **Array** tool. Choose the **Linear** button from the **Options Bar** and create an array of 7 components placed consecutively, as shown in Figure 9-18.

5. Repeat steps 1 to 4 and add the same parking component to the other seven places in the project. The site plan appears similar to the illustration shown in Figure 9-19.

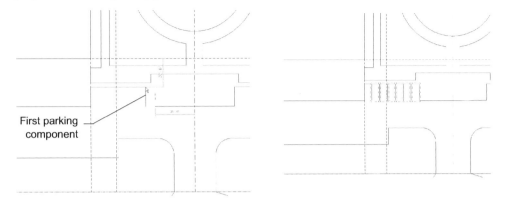

Figure 9-17 *Adding the parking component*   *Figure 9-18* *Creating an array of the parking components*

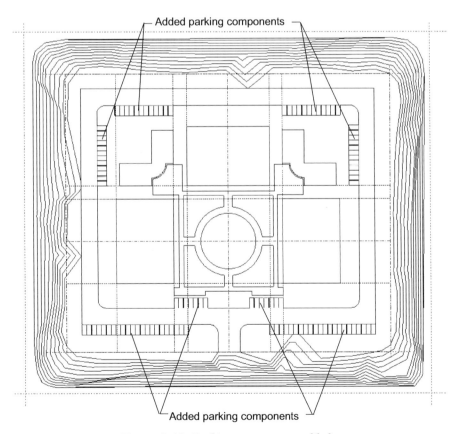

Figure 9-19 *Parking components added*

Adding Site Components

In this section, you will add site components from the in-built library of Autodesk Revit. The procedure is the same as that of adding parking components.

1. Choose the **Site Component** tool from the **Model Site** panel in the **Massing & Site** tab.

2. Next, you need to load the desired site component from the library. To do so, choose the **Load Family** tool from the **Mode** panel; the **Load Family** dialog box is displayed.

3. Now, browse to **US Imperial > Planting** and select **RPC Tree - Deciduous** and then choose **Open**.

4. Next, in the **Properties** palette, select the required option from the **Type Selector** drop-down list, as specified in the site component parameters for the project.
    For Imperial   **RPC Tree - Deciduous : Red Ash-25'**
    For Metric   **RPC Tree - Deciduous : Red Ash- 7.6 Metres**

5. Move the cursor to the site plan and click to add the planting component. Add multiple trees by clicking points on the site plan.

    The trees can be placed at an approximate location, as given in the sketch plan.

6. Next, select all trees from the site plan; the instance properties of the selected trees are displayed in the **Properties** palette.

7. Now, select **Level 2** from the drop-down list corresponding to the **Level** parameter.

    The complete site plan with site components appears similar to the illustration given in Figure 9-20.

Creating Sections through the Site

You can use the **Section** tool to create section lines horizontally and vertically through the site.

1. Choose the **View** tab and then invoke the **Section** tool from the **Create** panel.

2. Create horizontal section line from the left to the right across the center of the design scheme.

3. Similarly, create a vertical section line from the bottom to the top across the center. The two section lines are created and their corresponding views are added under the **Sections (Building Section)** head in the **Project Browser**.

4. Using the **Project Browser**, rename the horizontal section **Section1** as **Longitudinal Section** and the vertical section **Section 2** as **Transverse Section**.

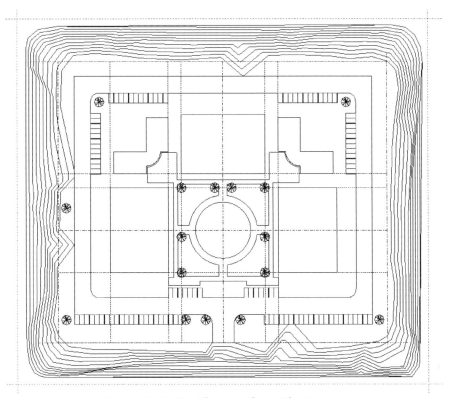

Figure 9-20 *Complete site plan with site components*

5. Double-click on **Longitudinal Section** under the **Sections (Building Section)** head in the **Project Browser** to view the longitudinal section.

6. Double-click on **Transverse Section** under the **Sections (Building Section)** head in the **Project Browser** to view the transverse section.

    You may need to increase the view range box by dragging the section box from the top or the bottom. Also, drag the levels to the sides of the section view. Ensure that the scale of the view shown in the **View Control Bar** is 1"=20'0" (1: 100).

7. Choose **Visual Styles > Shaded** from the **View Control Bar** to display the shaded view of the Longitudinal and Transverse sections, as shown in Figure 9-21 and Figure 9-22.

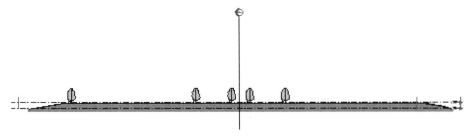

Figure 9-21 *Longitudinal section through the site*

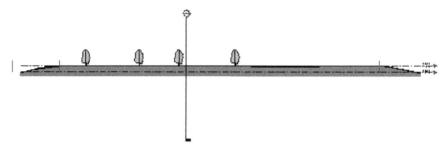

Figure 9-22 *Transverse section through the site*

8. Similarly, open the site plan and choose **Visual Styles > Shaded** from the **View Control Bar** to display the shaded view of the site plan, as shown in Figure 9-23.

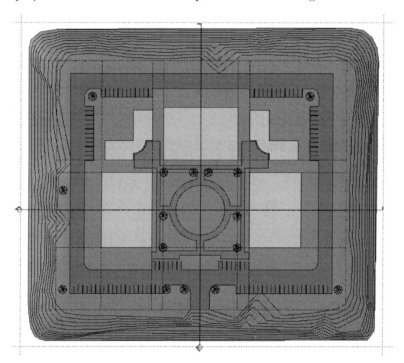

Figure 9-23 *Complete site plan*

Saving the Project

In this section, you will save the project file using the **Save As** tool.

1. Choose **Save As > Project** from the **File** menu to save the project. Specify the file name in the **File name** edit box and choose **Save**.

    For Imperial   **c09_SitePlan_tut1**
    For Metric   **M_c09_SitePlan_tut1**

    The project file is saved.

2. Choose **Close** from the **File** menu to close the project file.

Tip
*The modified material properties are not visible in the hidden lines view type. You can choose the **Visual Style** button in the **View Control Bar** and then choose **Shaded** option from the menu to graphically view the modified materials.*

EXERCISES

Exercise 1   Site Plan

Create the peripheral pedestrian walkway for the *Site Plan* project created in Tutorial 1 of this chapter, as shown in Figure 9-24. The sketch plan shows the pathway in white. You can assume the width of the walkway at various locations. Assign the material **Site - Sand** to the created pathway surface. Save the file as *c09_SitePlan_ex1.rvt (M_c09_SitePlan_ex1.rvt)*.

(Expected time: 30 min)

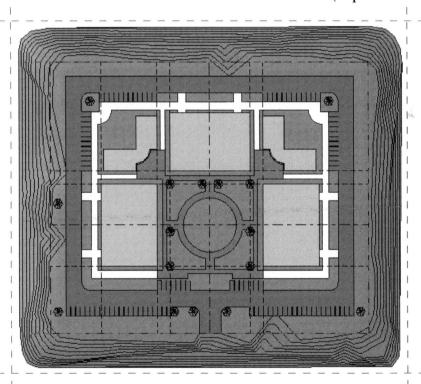

Figure 9-24 *Sketch plan for adding the peripheral pedestrian walkway to the Site Plan project*

This page is intentionally Left Blank

Chapter 10

Using Massing Tools

CREATING THE MASSING GEOMETRY

In Autodesk Revit, you can create the massing geometry in any of these three environments: Family Editor, Conceptual Design, and Project.

To create the massing geometry in the Family Editor environment, choose **New > Family** from the **File** menu; the **New Family - Select Template File** dialog box will be displayed. In this dialog box, choose the *Generic Model.rft* file (commonly used) from the **English_I** folder [for Metric the *Metric Generic Model.rft* file (commonly used) from the **English** folder] and then choose the **Open** button; a new file will open in the Family Editor environment. In the new file, create the massing geometry using various tools available in the ribbon. Various tools used to create a solid or a void geometry are as follows:

Extrusion
Revolve
Sweep
Blend
Swept Blend

Creating Cuts in a Massing Geometry by Using the Family Editor

You can cut a massing geometry by creating a void form in it. This void form is cut or subtracted from the massing geometry it intersects. You can create void forms by using the tools displayed in the **Void Forms** drop-down in the **Forms** panel of the **Create** tab. The **Void Forms** drop-down displays five tools: **Void Extrusion**, **Void Blend**, **Void Revolve**, **Void Swept Blend**, and **Void Sweep**. You can choose an appropriate tool to generate the shape and volume of the void form. The method of creating a void form using these tools is similar to that of creating a solid form. When any of the tools from the **Void Forms** drop-down is invoked, a contextual tab is displayed. For example, if you invoke the **Void Extrusion** tool, the **Modify | Create Void Extrusion** tab will be displayed. You can use the options in this tab to sketch the profile for the extruded void geometry. After sketching the profile of the extruded void geometry, choose the **Finish Edit Mode** button from the **Mode** panel of the **Modify | Create Void Extrusion** tab; the **Modify | Void Extrusion** tab will be displayed. From this tab, you can use various editing options to modify the extruded void geometry. Next, click in the drawing area or press ESC; the void form will automatically cut its shape and volume from the intersecting massing geometry.

Loading Massing Geometry into the Project

After creating massing geometries in the Family Editor, you can load them into the Project environment. To do so, choose the **Load into Project** tool from the **Family Editor** panel of the **Modify** tab; the current project file will appear if one project file is opened on the screen. Note that if more than one project file is opened in the current session, the **Load into Projects** dialog box will be displayed, as shown in Figure 10-1. In this dialog box, you can select the check box(es) to select the project(s) in which the created mass will be loaded. After selecting the required check box(es), choose **OK**; the mass will be loaded into the selected project file(s) corresponding to the check boxes selected. In this project file, the **Modify | Place Component** tab is chosen and you will notice that the mass created in the Family Editor appears in the drawing area along with the cursor.

Figure 10-1 The **Load into Projects** *dialog box*

Creating the In-Place Mass in a Project

In the Project environment, you have the option to create an in-place massing geometry by using the **In-Place Mass** tool. Invoke this tool from the **Conceptual Mass** panel of the **Massing & Site** tab; the **Name** dialog box will be displayed. In this dialog box, enter the name of the mass in the **Name** edit box and choose **OK**; the **Create** tab will be displayed. You can use the options in this tab to sketch the massing profile and convert it into a solid or void form. To sketch the profile for the mass, choose the **Model** tool from the **Draw** panel; the **Modify | Place Lines** tab will be displayed. You can use various sketching tools available in the **Draw** panel of this tab. While sketching, you can also use the **Reference Plane** tool from the **Draw** panel to draw references for the sketch. After sketching the profile, you can use any of the tools displayed in the **Create Form** drop-down in the **Form** panel. The **Create Form** drop-down displays two tools: **Solid Form** and **Void Form**. You can use the **Solid Form** tool to create a solid form and the **Void Form** tool to create a void form. To use any of the tools from the **Create Form** drop-down, you need to select the sketched profile from the drawing and then invoke the **Solid Form** or **Void Form** tool. After invoking any of these tools; the **Modify | Form** tab will be displayed. In this tab, you specify the settings to change the instance property of the mass created, divide the surfaces of the mass, and modify geometrical elements of the mass.

MASSING IN CONCEPTUAL DESIGN ENVIRONMENT

Conceptual design is the very first phase of a design process. The primary objective of a conceptual design is to create a representation of the idea generated for creating the building mass of a project. For creating a building project, conceptual design is very important for architects, engineers, and designers as it helps in finding out the final representation of the design intent. It thus enables them to create more specific sets of plans.

TUTORIALS

Tutorial 1   Office Building 2

In this tutorial, you will create massing geometry for a five-story office building based on the shape shown in Figure 10-2. It consists of a 50'0" X 50'0" (15240 X 15240 mm) central hall that is 60'0"(18288 mm) high. It has a 30'0"(9144 mm) diameter cylindrical atrium with a hemispherical dome at the top level. The central hall is flanked by the right and left wings that are 40'0"(12192 mm) high. The entrance area is 30'0"(9144 mm) high. Use the dimensions of the building given in the floor plan shown in Figure 10-3 and the dimensions of the elevation shown in Figure 10-4. The dimensions and the text have been given for reference and are not to be created. After creating the massing geometry, convert it into building elements with the parameters given next.   **(Expected time: 1 hr 15 min)**

1. Project parameters:
    For Imperial   Template File- *default.rte*,
                         File name to be assigned- *c10_Office-2_tut1.rvt*
                         Floor to floor height of the building - **10'0"**

    For Metric   Template File- *DefaultMetric.rte*,
                         File name to be assigned- *M_c10_Office-2_tut1.rvt*
                         Floor to floor height of the building - **3048 mm**

2. Building Element types for the converted shell elements:
    For Imperial   Floor: **Floor : LW Concrete on Metal Deck**
                         Walls: Central Hall- **Basic Wall: Exterior - Brick on CMU**
                         Left and Right Wing, and Entrance- **Curtain Wall: Exterior Glazing**
                         (Spacing 5'0" horizontal, 10'0" vertical)
                         Flat Roof: **Roof : Generic 9"**

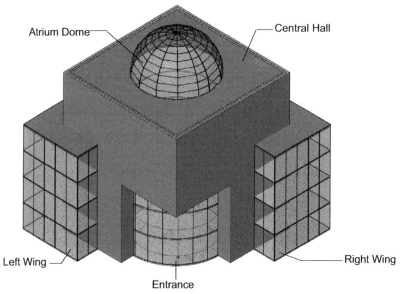

Figure 10-2 *3D sketch view of the office building*

Curtain system for dome: Spacing **3'6"** horizontal, **7'0"** vertical; Mullion type

For Metric   Floor: **Floor : LW Concrete on Metal Deck**
　　　　　　 Walls: Central Hall- **Basic Wall: Exterior - Brick on CMU**
　　　　　　 Left and Right Wing, and Entrance- **Curtain Wall: Exterior Glazing**
　　　　　　 (Spacing 1524 mm horizontal, 3048 mm vertical)
　　　　　　 Flat Roof: **Roof : Generic 400 mm**
Curtain system for dome: Spacing **1067 mm** horizontal, **2134 mm** vertical; Mullion type

The following steps are required to complete this tutorial:

a.   Open a new project file by using the default template file and adding levels.
b.   Create a massing geometry using the **Form** tool, refer to Figures 10-5 through 10-8.
c.   Cut the geometry based on the sketch plan to create the atrium and the entrance using the **Void Form** tool, refer to Figures 10-9 through 10-12.
d.   Use the **Solid Form** tool to generate the atrium dome, refer to Figures 10-13 through 10-15.
e.   Convert the massing geometry into the specified building elements, refer to Figures 10-16 through 10-20.
f.   Save the project using the **Save As** tool.
　　　　 For Imperial   *c10_Office-2_tut1.rvt*
　　　　 For Metric　 *M_c10_Office-2_tut1.rvt*
g.   Close the project.

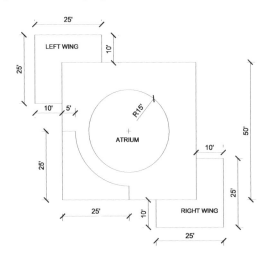

Figure 10-3 *Sketch plan for the office building*

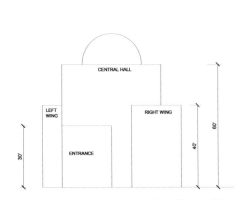

Figure 10-4 *Elevation for the office building*

Opening the Project File and Adding Levels

You need to first open a new project file using the **New** tool. As the building is five-story high, you need to create four additional levels and rename them according to the floor levels.

1.   Choose **New > Project** from the **File** menu; the **New Project** dialog box is displayed.

2. Select the **Architectural Template** option from the drop-down list in the **Template file** area, if it is not selected by default.

3. Choose the **OK** button to close the **New Project** dialog box; the new project file is opened in the drawing window.

4. In the **Project Browser**, double-click on **South** in the **Elevations (Building Elevation)** head to display the corresponding view.

5. Choose the **Level** tool from the **Datum** panel in the **Architecture** tab.

6. Add four levels above level 2 at an elevation of **10'0" (3048 mm)** each. (For more information on adding levels, refer to Adding Levels section in Chapter 6)

7. Rename the levels as follows:
   Level 1- First Floor
   Level 2- Second Floor
   Level 3- Third Floor
   Level 4- Fourth Floor
   Level 5- Fifth Floor
   Level 6- Roof

   Choose the **Yes** button in the **Revit** conformation box to rename the corresponding views.

Creating the Massing Geometry

Now, you can start creating the massing geometry using the tools for massing. The central hall and the two wings can be generated using the **Form** tool.

Note
The massing geometry can be created using different methods and tools. The steps given below describe a general procedure to create massing geometry. The steps and methods may vary depending on the design intent.

1. Double-click on the **First Floor** under the **Floor Plans** head in the **Project Browser** to display the corresponding plan.

2. Choose the **In-Place Mass** tool from the **Conceptual Mass** panel of the **Massing & Site** tab; the **Massing - Show Mass Enabled** message box is displayed.

3. Choose **Close** from this message box; the **Name** dialog box is displayed.

4. In the **Name** edit box of the **Name** dialog box, enter the name **Central Hall** and then choose the **OK** button.

5. Invoke the **Rectangle** sketching tool from the **Draw** panel of the **Create** tab.

6. Move the cursor in the area lying in the mid of the four elevation tags and sketch a square with **50'0"(15240 mm)** side. After sketching the square, choose the **Modify** button.

7. Now, select the created square and choose the **Solid Form** tool from **Modify|Lines > Form > Create Form** drop-down; the **Modify |Form** tab is displayed.

8. Next, choose the **Default 3D** tool from the **Create** panel of the **View** tab; the 3D view of the mass created is displayed.

9. Now, move the cursor over the top face of the box created, refer to Figure 10-5, and click when the edges of the faces are highlighted. On doing so, two temporary dimensions are highlighted.

10. Click on the value of the lower dimension (dimension that specifies the height of the box) and enter **60' (18288 mm)** in the edit box. Now, press ENTER; the box is resized to the height 60' (18288 mm).

11. Choose the **Modify** button and then right-click in the drawing area; a shortcut menu is displayed. Choose **Zoom To Fit** from the shortcut menu; the box created can now be viewed completely.

12. Now, choose the **Finish Mass** button from the **In-Place Editor** panel of the **Modify** tab; the Central Hall massing is created.

Similarly, you need to create the left and right wings of the building using the **Form** tool. You will sketch the profile in the first floor plan view and extrude it to a height of **40'0"** (**12192 mm**), as specified in the sketch plan.

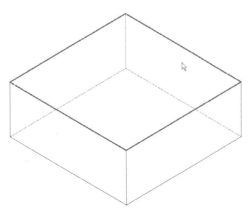

Figure 10-5 Selecting the top face of the central hall

13. Create the mass for left and right wings of the building. Double-click on **First Floor** under the **Floor Plans** head in the **Project Browser** to display the corresponding plan.

14. Now, choose the **In-Place Mass** tool from the **Conceptual Mass** panel of the **Massing & Site** tab; the **Name** dialog box is displayed.

15. In the **Name** dialog box, enter the name **Wings** and choose the **OK** button.

16. Invoke the **Line** tool from the **Draw** panel of the **Create** tab and ensure that the **Chain** check box is selected in the **Options Bar**.

17. Move the cursor near the lower right corner of the square and sketch the profile based on the dimensions given in the sketch plan, refer to Figure 10-4. The profile for the right wing is sketched, as shown in Figure 10-6.

    Note that the sketch for the wings should be a closed sketch.

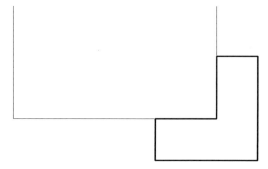

Figure 10-6 Sketched profile for the right wing

18. Choose the **Modify** button from the **Select** panel to clear the current selection.

19. Now, select the sketched profile for the right wing and choose the **Mirror - Draw Axis** tool from the **Modify** panel of the **Modify | Lines** tab.

20. Draw a line from the top right corner to the bottom left corner of the central square to define the mirror axis line. The profile is mirrored at the diagonally opposite corners of the square, as shown in Figure 10-7.

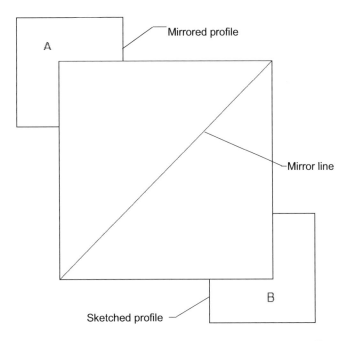

A

Mirrored profile

Mirror line

Sketched profile

B

Figure 10-7 Creating a mirror copy of the sketched profile

21. Now, ensure that the mirrored profile is selected and the **Modify | Lines** tab is chosen.

22. Choose the **Solid Form** tool from the **Modify | Lines > Form > Create Form** drop-down.

23. Next, select the other profile at the lower right corner and repeat step 22.

24. Choose the **Modify** button from the **Select** panel and then choose the **Default 3D** tool from the **Create** panel of the **View** tab; the 3D view of the mass created is displayed.

25. Now move the cursor over the top face of the created mass marked as A (refer to Figure 10-7) and then click on the face when it is highlighted. On doing so, two temporary dimensions are displayed.

26. Click on the value of the lower displayed dimension and enter **40'** (**12192mm**) in the edit box.

27. After entering the value in the edit box, press ENTER; the selected face of the mass will be extended to a height of 40' from the First Floor level and the mass corresponding to it is resized.

28. Next, select the top face of the other mass marked B and repeat steps 25 to 27.

29. Now, after you create the masses for the wings, choose the **Modify** button in the **Select** panel; the current selection is cleared.

30. Now, choose the **Finish Mass** button from the **In-Place Editor** panel of the **Modify** tab; the masses for the wings are created.

31. Now, move the cursor over the **ViewCube** tool and right-click; a shortcut menu is displayed. Choose **Orient to a Direction > Northeast Isometric** from the shortcut menu; the 3D view of the created mass geometry is displayed, as shown in Figure 10-8.

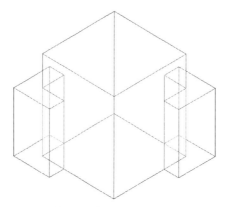

*Figure 10-8 The **Northeast Isometric** view of the central hall and the two wings*

Cutting the Massing Geometry

After creating the desired building blocks, you can now cut them to create the atrium and the entrance. The **Void Form** tool can be used to create the desired void geometry.

1. Double-click on **First Floor** under the **Floor Plans** head in the **Project Browser** to display the first floor plan view.

2. Choose the **Central Square** hall; the **Modify | Mass** tab is displayed.

3. Choose the **Edit In-Place** tool from the **Model** panel of the **Modify | Mass** tab; the **Modify** tab is displayed.

4. Next, choose **Visual Style > Wireframe** from **View Control Bar**.

5. Draw reference planes diagonally to locate the center of the square by using the **Plane** tool from the **Draw** panel of the **Modify** tab. After creating the reference planes, choose the **Modify** button from the **Select** panel to clear the current selection.

6. Now, invoke the **Circle** tool from the **Draw** panel of the **Modify** tab.

7. Move the cursor at the center of the square. Use the reference planes to locate the center and click to specify it.

8. Move the cursor to the right and enter the value **15'0"** (**4572mm**). Next, press ENTER; the circle of **30'0"** diameter is created. Now, press ESC twice to exit and then select the circle created.

9. Choose the **Void Form** tool from the **Modify | Lines > Form > Create Form** drop-down; two circular images are displayed.

10. Choose the left image and then choose the **View** tab. Next, choose the **Default 3D** tool from the **Create** panel; the 3D view of the mass created is displayed.

11. Now, select the two segments of the circle profile of the void created by using the CTRL key, as shown in Figure 10-9. On selecting the segments, the corresponding pivot points are displayed. Hold and drag the blue segments till they cross the upper face of the central hall. Choose the **Modify** button.

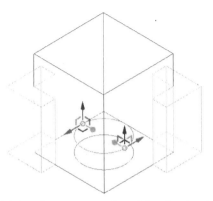

Figure 10-9 *The segments selected for the circular void*

12. Now, double-click on **First Floor** under the **Floor Plans** head in the **Project Browser** to display the corresponding plan.

13. Next, choose the **Modify| Form** tab and invoke the **Center-ends Arc** tool from the **Draw** panel.

14. Move the cursor to the center of the atrium circle and then click. Next, move the cursor horizontally toward the left and enter the value **20'0"** (**6096mm**) to specify the radius. Now, press ENTER.

15. Move the cursor counterclockwise and click to create a quarter arc, as shown in Figure 10-10.

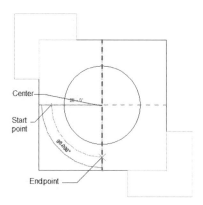

Figure 10-10 *Sketching an arc to create a cutting geometry*

16. Choose the **Line** sketching tool and ensure that the **Chain** check box is selected.

17. Sketch the profile of the cutting geometry, as shown in Figure 10-11.

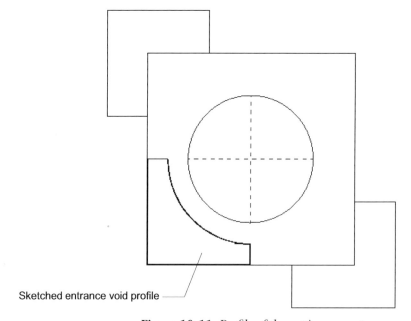

Figure 10-11 *Profile of the cutting geometry*

18. Choose the **Modify** button from the **Select** panel and then select the profile that was created recently; the **Modify|Lines** tab is displayed.

19. Choose the **Void Form** tool from the **Modify | Lines > Form > Create Form** drop-down; the void mass is created.

20. Next, choose the **View** tab and then choose the **Default 3D** tool from the **Create** panel; the 3D view of the created mass is displayed.

21. Now, move and place the cursor over the **ViewCube** tool and right-click; a shortcut menu is displayed.

22. Choose **Orient to a Direction > Front Left Isometric** from the shortcut menu.

23. Next, select the top face of the void geometry created, as shown in Figure 10-12.

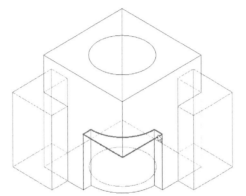

Figure 10-12 Selecting the face of the void geometry to edit the height

24. After selecting the top face, click on the dimension value of the temporary dimension that is displayed at the bottom. Enter **30'** in the displayed edit box and press ENTER.

25. Now, choose the **Modify** button from the **Select** panel and then choose the **Finish Mass** button from the **In-Place Editor** panel of the **Modify** tab.

26. Next, right-click on the drawing area and choose **Zoom To Fit** from the shortcut menu.

Creating the Atrium Dome

The atrium dome can be added using the **Form** tool. It is a hemispherical dome having a radius of **20'0"(6096 mm)** which is same as the radius of the atrium.

1. Choose the **In-Place Mass** tool from the **Conceptual Mass** panel of the **Massing & Site** tab; the **Name** dialog box is displayed.

2. In this dialog box, enter **Dome** in the **Name** edit box and choose the **OK** button.

3. Choose the **Set** tool from the **Work Plane** panel of the **Create** tab; you are prompted to pick a plane.

4. Select the right side entrance wall as the work plane, as shown in Figure 10-13. Note that to confirm that the selected face has been assigned the current work plane, choose the **Show** button from the **Work Plane** panel of the **Create** tab; the selected plane is highlighted.

5. Now, choose the **Reference** tool from the **Draw** panel of the **Create** tab and invoke the **Line** tool.

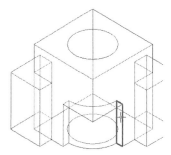

Figure 10-13 Selecting the right side entrance wall as the work plane

6. Sketch the reference lines for the dome, as shown in Figure 10-14.

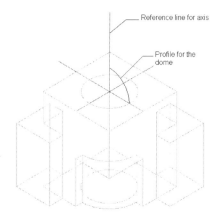

Figure 10-14 The reference line and the profile for the dome

7. Now, choose the **Model** tool from the **Draw** panel of the **Modify** tab and then invoke the **Center-ends Arc** sketching tool from the **Draw** panel.

8. Using the center of the atrium roof as the center of the curve, sketch a quarter arc, refer to Figure 10-14. Next, choose the **Modify** button to clear the current selection.

9. Select the reference line that defines the vertical axis and then select the arc using the CTRL key, refer to Figure 10-14.

10. Now, choose the **Solid Form** tool from the **Form** panel; the dome is created, as shown in Figure 10-15.

11. Choose the **Finish Mass** button from the **In-Place Editor** panel of the **Modify** tab to finish the creation of the dome geometry. Ignore the warning message displayed, if any. Now, choose the **Modify** button from the **Select** panel.

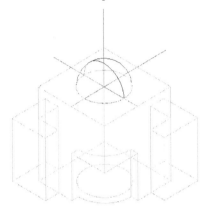

Figure 10-15 *The dome created for the Atrium*

Converting Massing Geometry into Building Elements

You can now convert the massing geometry into building elements using the **Floor**, **Wall**, and **Roof** tools. In order to create floors, you must first create different floor area faces.

1. Select the **Central Hall** and **Wings** massing geometries by holding the CTRL key; the **Modify | Mass** tab is displayed.

2. Choose the **Mass Floors** tool from the **Model** panel; the **Mass Floors** dialog box is displayed.

3. In the **Mass Floors** dialog box, select the check boxes for all the floors and choose the **OK** button; the floor area faces are created for the selected floors. Now, choose the **Modify** button.

4. Next, choose the **Floor** tool from the **Model by Face** panel of the **Massing & Site** tab; the **Modify | Place Floor by Face** tab is displayed.

5. In the **Properties** palette, select **Floor: LW Concrete on Metal Deck** (for Metric **160mm Concrete with 50mm Metal Deck**) from the **Type Selector** drop-down list.

6. Using the crossing window, select all the floor faces and then choose the **Create Floor** tool from the **Multiple Selection** panel; Autodesk Revit creates floors at the floor area faces. Now, choose **Visual Style > Shaded** from the **View Control Bar**. The shaded view of the model is shown in Figure 10-16.

7. Now, choose the **Wall** tool from the **Model by Face** panel of the **Massing & Site** tab; the **Modify | Place Wall** tab is displayed.

8. In the **Properties** palette, select the **Basic Wall : Exterior - Brick on CMU** wall type from the **Type Selector** drop-down list.

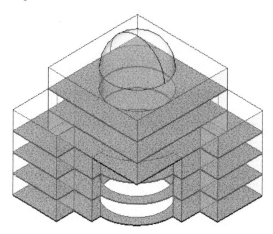

Figure 10-16   *Floor areas of the massing converted into floors*

9. Now, move the cursor over the central hall massing geometry and when an exterior wall is highlighted, click to convert the wall face into the selected wall type.

10. Similarly, click on the other exterior walls of the central hall including the two side walls of the entrance. The resultant 3D view is shown in Figure 10-17.

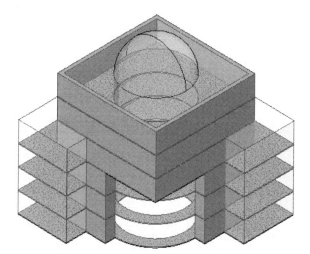

Figure 10-17 *Converting the massing into walls*

11. Next, in the **Properties** palette, select the **Curtain Wall : Exterior Glazing** wall type from the **Type Selector** drop-down list.

12. Choose the **Edit Type** button in the **Properties** palette; the **Type Properties** dialog box is displayed.

13. In the **Type Properties** dialog box, enter **5'0"(1524 mm)** in the **Value** field of the **Spacing** parameter in the **Vertical Grid** category and **10'0"(3048 mm)** for the **Spacing** parameter in the **Horizontal Grid** category.

14. Now, choose **Apply** and **OK**; the **Type Properties** dialog box is closed and the specified parameters are applied to the selected type.

15. Next, highlight and click on the exterior walls of the right and left wings to convert them into the selected exterior glazing walls.

16. Similarly, convert the curved entrance wall into the exterior glazing wall type. The 3D view now appears similar to the illustration shown in Figure 10-18. Now, choose the **Modify** button.

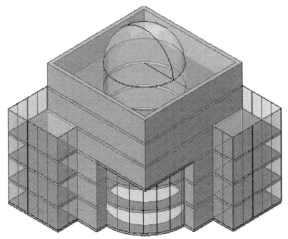

Figure 10-18 Converting the entrance wall massing into walls

17. Next, choose the **Roof** tool from the **Model by Face** panel of the **Massing & Site** tab; the **Modify | Place Roof by Face** tab is displayed.

18. In the **Type Selector** drop-down list, select the specified roof type.
    For Imperial   **Basic Roof : Generic - 9"**
    For Metric   **Basic Roof : Generic - 300 mm**

19. Highlight the roof face of the central hall and click.

20. Now, choose the **Create Roof** tool from the **Multiple Selection** panel of the **Modify | Place Roof by Face** tab; the roof is created on the selected face.

21. Similarly, create the roof of the same type for the two wings. After creating the roofs, the 3D view appears similar to the one shown in Figure 10-19. Next, you will create the curtain wall system for the dome.

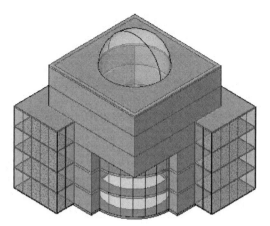

Figure 10-19 *Converting the massing into roof*

22. To create a curtain system for the dome, choose the **Curtain System** tool from the **Model by face** panel of the **Massing & Site** tab; the **Modify | Place Curtain System by Face** tab is displayed.

23. Choose the **Type Properties** tool from the **Properties** panel; the **Type Properties** dialog box is displayed.

24. Choose the **Duplicate** button; the **Name** dialog box is displayed. Enter **3'6" X 7'0" (1067 x 2134 mm)** in the edit box and then choose the **OK** button.

25. Enter the values **7'0" (2134 mm)** and **3'6"(1067 mm)** in the **Value** fields of the **Spacing** parameters under the **Grid 1 Pattern** and **Grid 2 Pattern** categories, respectively.

26. Choose the **OK** button; the **Type Properties** dialog box is closed.

27. Now, select both the curved faces of the dome and then choose the **Create System** tool from the **Multiple Selection** panel of the **Modify | Place Curtain System by Face** tab. The curved surfaces of the dome are converted into curtain systems. Now, choose the **Modify** button.

28. Next, you need to add a door to the entrance. To start with, choose the **Insert** tab and then choose the **Load Family** tool from the **Load from Library** panel; the **Load Family** dialog box is displayed.

29. In this dialog box, browse to the **US Imperial > Doors** folder and then choose the **Door-Curtain-Wall-Double-Glass** (for Metric M_**Door-Curtain-Wall-Double-Glass**) family file. After choosing the file, choose **Open**; the selected file is loaded in the drawing.

30. Choose the **Modify** button and then select the two curtain panels of the exterior glazing by the window selection process.

31. Invoke the **Filter** tool from the right end of the Status Bar; the **Filter** dialog box is displayed.

32. In the **Filter** dialog box, clear all the check boxes except the **Curtain Panel** check box and then choose the **OK** button; the **Filter** dialog box is closed and selection is done, as shown in Figure 10-20.

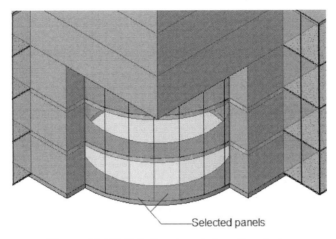

Figure 10-20 Selecting panels from the glazing

33. From the **Type Selector** drop-down list, select the **Curtain Wall Door-Curtain-Wall--Double-Glass** option. Next, choose the **Modify** button.

34. To add mullions to the exterior glazing, choose the **Mullion** tool from the **Build** panel of the **Architecture** tab; the **Modify |Place Mullion** tab is displayed.

35. In the **Type Selector** drop-down list, select the desired mullion type.
    For Imperial   **Rectangular Mullion : 1" Square**
    For Metric   **Rectangular Mullion : 30 mm Square**.

36. Next, choose the **All Grid Lines** tool from the **Placement** panel and move the cursor over the exterior glazings. Click on each face of the glazing when it is highlighted. Add all the curtain systems to the project, including the exterior wing walls, the curved entrance wall, and the dome. Use the **Grid Line Segment** tool from the **Placement** panel to add grids, if required.

    The completed 3D view of the project appears similar to the one shown in Figure 10-20.

Saving the Project
In this section, you will save the project file using the **Save As** tool.

1. Choose **Save As > Project** from the **File** menu; the **Save As** dialog box is displayed.

2. Enter **c10_Office-2_tut1** in the **File name** edit box and choose **Save**; the file is saved.

3. Now, choose **Close** from the **File** menu to close the Autodesk Revit session.

EXERCISES

Exercise 1 Office

Create a massing geometry for an office building that consists of two identical 400'0" high towers with a connecting passage at 200'0" height. Each tower has a 50'0" X 50'0" base with an offset of 5'0" at 200'0" and 300'0" levels. There are two masts on each tower with a base radius of 2'6" and the top radius of 0'6" The connecting passage is 150'0" long and has a width and height of 25'0" with a vault roof. The plan view of the building is shown in Figure 10-21. The 3D, elevation, and shaded views of the building are shown in Figures 10-22, 10-23, and 10-24, respectively. The dimensions and text have been given for reference and are not to be created. Assume the missing dimensions proportionate to the building design. After creating the massing, convert it into the building elements with the parameters given next.

(Expected time: 45 min)

1. Project file parameters:
   Template File- **Architectural Template**,
   File Name to be assigned- *c10_OfficeTowers_ex1.rvt*

2. Building element types for the converted shell elements:
   Floor: **Floor : LW Concrete on Metal Deck**
   Walls: Towers- **Curtain Wall: Exterior Glazing**
   (horizontal and vertical spacing- 10'0")
   Connecting Passage- **Curtain Wall: Curtain Wall 1**
   Roof: **Basic Roof : Generic 9"**

After completion, the building model will appear similar to the illustration given in Figure 10-21.

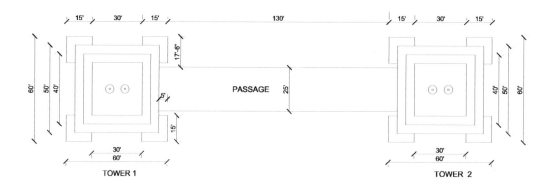

Figure 10-21 *Sketch plan for a multistory office building*

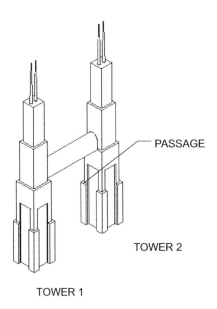

Figure 10-22 *3D view of the building*

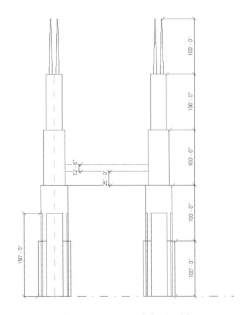

Figure 10-23 *Elevation view of the building*

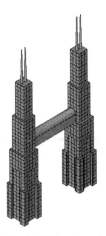

Figure 10-24 *Shaded 3D view of the building*

Exercise 2   Stadium

Create a massing geometry for a Stadium. Its plan view is shown in Figure 10-25. It consists of the field area and stands. In the stands, the tread of the lower tier is 3'0" and the riser is 1'0". Similarly, the tread of the lower-tier is 3'0"and the riser is 1'6". The cross-section view of stands is shown in Figure 10-26. Assume the missing dimensions proportionate to the sketch plan. Use the following building parameters.

(Expected time: 30 min)

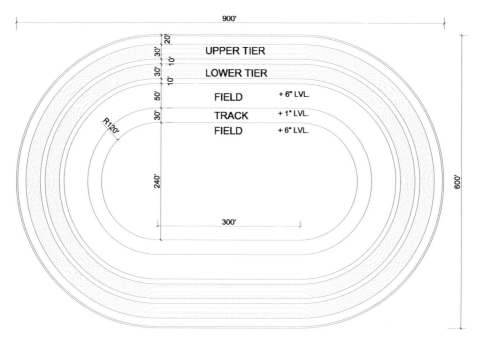

Figure 10-25 *Sketch plan of the Stadium*

1. Project file Parameters:
    Template file- **Architectural Template**,
    File name to be assigned- *c10_Stadium_ex2.rvt*

    After completion, the building model will appear similar to the illustration given in
    Figure 10-27.

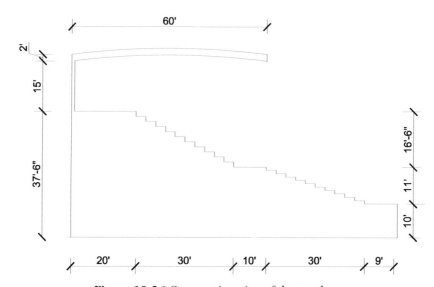

Figure 10-26 *Cross-section view of the stands*

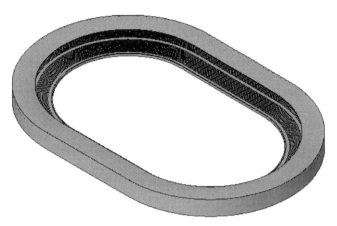

Figure 10-27 3D view of the stadium

This page is intentionally left Blank

Chapter *11*

Adding Annotations
and Dimensions

Learning Objectives

After completing this chapter, you will be able to:

• *Add tags to building elements using the Tag tool*
• *Add room tags to the interior spaces using the Room Tag tool*
• *Add symbols to project view using the Symbol tool*
• *Create dimensions using various dimensioning tools*

ADDING TAGS

You can easily tag various elements in a building model. A tag is a useful annotation that assists in identifying the tagged building element. When you design complex building models using Autodesk Revit, tags play an important role in arranging various elements in schedules. You can then add necessary description for each tagged element in a tabulated form. Figure 11-1 shows the usage of various tags in an interior layout.

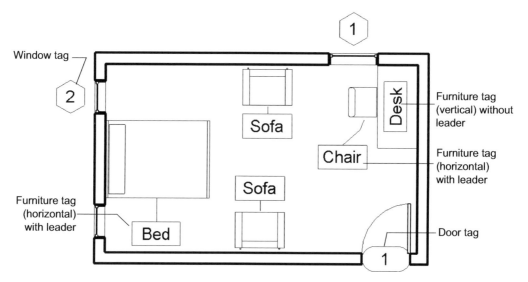

Figure 11-1 Various tags in an interior layout

Autodesk Revit provides various tools that are used to add and edit tags. When you open the default template file, tags of a certain category of elements are preloaded. Therefore, when you add the elements such as doors and windows, Autodesk Revit automatically tags them. For the other elements, you need to load their respective tags from the Autodesk Revit library. Like other annotations, tags are also view-specific and they appear only in the view they have been created in. You can control the visibility of tags by choosing the **Visibility/ Graphics** tool from the **Graphics** panel of the **View** tab. On doing so, the **Visibility/Graphic Overrides for <current view >** dialog box will be displayed. The **Annotation Categories** tab of this dialog box contains the list of tag categories such as **Door Tags**, **Window Tags**, **Furniture Tags**, **Electrical Fixture Tags**, and so on. You can select the appropriate check boxes to control the visibility of each category of tags. The methods used for tagging the elements are described next.

ROOM TAGS

Room tags are useful annotation tools for your drawing and they help you set information about the type of occupancy and define the enclosed area and volume. Autodesk Revit enables you to define and add a nomenclature to various interior and exterior spaces in a building project. This is important not only for identifying each space, but also for creating a room-wise project schedule. In Autodesk Revit, a room is also treated as an element of the project similar to the other elements such as a wall, door, or window.

ADDING SYMBOLS

| **Ribbon:** | Annotate > Symbol > Symbol |

The **Symbol** tool is used to add 2D annotation drawing symbols to a project view to make it more informative. For example, you can use the **Symbol** tool to insert a north symbol, graphical scale, centerline symbol, and so on into a specific project view. Like other annotations, symbols are also view-specific in character.

When you choose the **Symbol** tool from the **Symbol** panel, the **Modify | Place Symbol** tab will be displayed. Now, from the **Type Selector** drop-down list which shows the loaded symbols in the project, select the required symbol. The instance and type properties depend on the selected symbol. You can modify the instance and type properties of a symbol from the **Properties** palette. The **Number of Leaders** spinner available in the **Options Bar** enables you to add multiple leaders to a single symbol. If the **Rotate after placement** check box is selected, the **Rotate** tool will be invoked as soon as you place the symbol. As a result, you can reorient the symbol after placing it.

The selected symbol can be added to the project view by clicking at the desired location. Figure 11-2 shows an example of the centerline symbol added to a plan view. Multiple instances of the symbol can then be placed by clicking on the locations of other instances.

Figure 11-2 *Adding the centerline symbol to the plan view*

ADDING DIMENSIONS

Dimensions play a crucial role in the presentation of a project. Although the building model conveys the graphical image of the design, yet to materialize it at the site, the building view must provide information and statistics regarding each element. Since the design drawing is used for the actual construction of a project, it is essential to describe the building parts in terms of actual measurement parameters such as length, width, height, angle, radius, diameter, and so on. All these information can be added into the project using dimensions. The information conveyed through dimensions is, in most cases, as important as the project view itself. It ensures that the project drawings are read and interpreted in appropriate way. Adding dimensions also ensures that there are no discrepancies between various elements used in the generation of the building drawings.

Types of Dimensions

In Autodesk Revit, you can use two types of dimensions: temporary and permanent. By default, the temporary and permanent dimensions use the units settings specified in the initial start-up of the project. The temporary dimensions are not view-specific, whereas the permanent dimensions are view-specific. It means that if you change the view, the permanent dimensions will not be visible. These two types of dimensions are discussed in detail in the next section.

Temporary Dimensions
Permanent Dimensions

Adding Permanent Dimensions

Permanent dimensions are added specifically for a particular measurement. In Autodesk Revit, you can access various dimensioning tools from the **Dimension** panel in the **Annotate** tab, as shown in Figure 11-3. You can choose the appropriate dimension type and the dimension tool to add dimensions to the element.

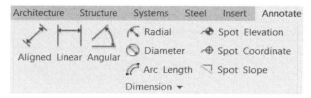

Figure 11-3 Dimensioning tools in the
Dimension *panel of the* ***Annotate*** *tab*

Aligned Dimensions
Linear Dimensions
Angular Dimensions
Radial Dimensions
Diametric Dimensions
Arc Length Dimensions

TUTORIAL

Tutorial 1   Apartment 1

In this tutorial, you will first add rooms to the enclosed spaces of the *Apartment 1* project created in Tutorial 1 of Chapter 8, and then name the rooms by using the **Room Tag** tool. You will also tag the furniture and then dimension the ground floor plan view based on the sketch plan shown in Figure 11-4. The dimensions shown on the top and right sides of the plan are referenced to the wall centerlines, whereas the dimensions on the bottom and left side are referenced to the wall faces. The exact location of the tags and dimensions is not important in this tutorial. Use the parameters given below for creating the dimensions.

(Expected time: 45 min)

1. Room tag- **Room Tag: Boxed**

2. Furniture tag- **Furniture Tag: Standard** with leader arrowhead- **Arrow 30 Degree**

3. Dimension Parameters:
   Dimension type to be based on the following options:
   For Imperial   **Linear w Center - 3/32" Arial** and **Linear - 3/32" Arial**
   For Metric   **Diagonal Center - 2.5 mm Arial** and **Linear - 3/32" Arial**

   New dimension type names- **Linear Dimension - CL** and **Linear Dimension - Faces**
   Tick Mark-   For Imperial   **Dot Filled 1/16"**
                     For Metric   **Filled Dot 3mm**
   Witness Line Gap to Element-   For Imperial   **1/4"**
                                           For Metric   **6.35mm**

The following steps are required to complete this tutorial:

a. Open the specified project file and the first floor plan view.
b. Use the **Room** and **Room Tag** tools and add rooms and room tags, refer to Figures 11-5 through 11-9.
c. Invoke the **Tag** tool and then load and add the furniture tags, refer to Figures 11-10 through 11-13.
d. Invoke the **Dimension** tool and set the type parameters.
e. Add dimensions to the project plan view using the wall centerlines as the reference, refer to Figures 11-14 through 11-16.
f. Add dimensions using automatic dimensioning with wall faces as the reference, refer to Figure 11-18.
g. Save the project using the **Save As** tool.
          For Imperial   *c11_Apartment1_tut1.rvt*
          For Metric   *M_c11_Apartment1_tut1.rvt*
h. Close the project.

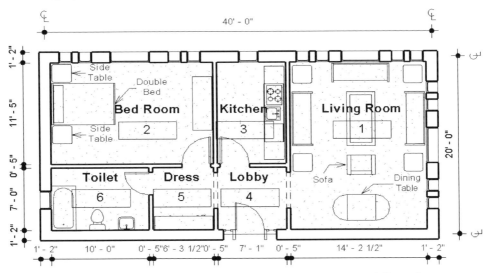

Figure 11-4 *Sketch plan for adding room tags, furniture tags, and dimensions to the Apartment 1 project*

Opening the Project File

1. To begin this tutorial, open the file that you have created in Tutorial 1 of Chapter 8 for the *Apartment 1* project.

   Choose **Open > Project** from the **File** menu and open *c08_Apartment1_tut1.rvt for imperial (M_c08_Apartment1_tut1.rvt for metric)*. You can also download this file from *http://www.cadsofttech.com*. The path of the file is as follows: *Textbooks > Civil/GIS > Revit Architecture > Revit Architecture 2019 For Novices*.

2. After you open the file, double-click on **First Floor** in the **Floor Plans** head from the **Project Browser**; the first floor plan is displayed.

Adding Room and Room Tags

In this section of the tutorial, you will first add rooms (without a tag) to the enclosed space. To add room tags to the interior spaces, you need to invoke the **Room Tag** tool. The room tag is preloaded in the default template file. As this template will be used in this tutorial, you do not need to load it. Next, you need to move the cursor inside the enclosed space and click to add the room tag. You can then click on the tag and rename it. Autodesk Revit sequentially numbers the room tags. Therefore, you need to add them based on the sequence given in the sketch plan.

Note

In a building project, you can add rooms with tags attached to them and then rename the tags according to the space functionality. In this section of the tutorial, the rooms are added without tags and then the tags are added to make you understand the use of the **Room** *tool and the* **Room Tag** *tool separately.*

1. Invoke the **Room** tool from the **Room & Area** panel in the **Architecture** tab; the **Modify | Place Room** tab is displayed. Now, as you move the cursor in the drawing area, you will notice a blue rectangle along with the default text **Room** attached to it. Next, you need to ensure that while adding rooms, the tags should not appear.

   Note that the **Tag on Placement** button is not chosen in the **Tag** panel.

2. Move the cursor inside the living room (for location, refer to Figure 11-5, and click in the enclosed space. Notice that when you move inside the enclosed space, it is shaded with blue color and the shading becomes transparent. Also notice that the room is marked by two diagonal lines and a rectangle showing the extent of the enclosed space.

3. Without exiting the **Room** tool, repeat step 2 to add room to the kitchen, toilet, bed room, dress, and lobby, refer to Figure 11-4. Note that after adding the last room, you need to press ESC to exit.

4. After adding the rooms to the spaces, you need to tag them. Choose the **Room Tag** tool from the **Tag** panel of the **Annotate** tab; the **Modify | Place Room Tag** tab is displayed. Notice that when you invoke the **Room Tag** tool, all rooms in the drawing are displayed in a blue transparent shade with the diagonal lines showing their extents.

5. Move the cursor inside the living room; a Room tag attached to the cursor is displayed, as shown in Figure 11-5. Click to add the tag, as shown in Figure 11-6. Now, press ESC to exit from the **Room Tag** tool.

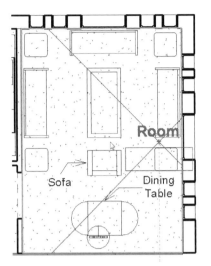

Figure 11-5 *Preview of the room tag and the highlighted room boundary*

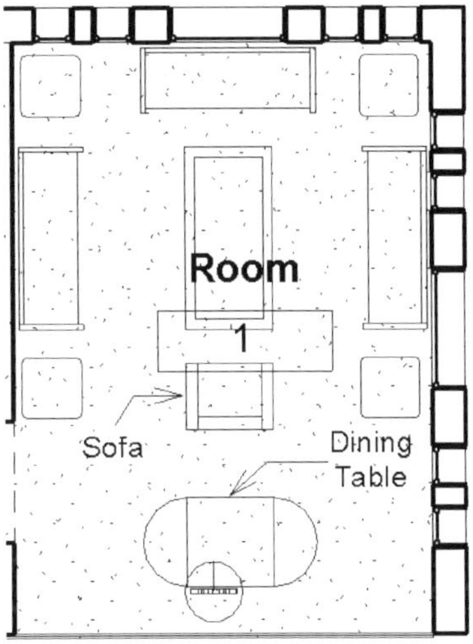

Figure 11-6 *The room tag added*

6. Select the room tag marked **1**(in the living room) and click on the text **Room**; an edit box is displayed.

7. Type **Living Room** in the edit box, as shown in Figure 11-7. Now, press ENTER and then ESC. The room tag is renamed, as shown in Figure 11-8.

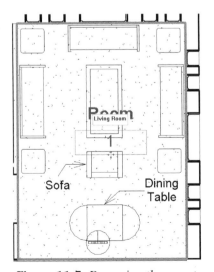

Figure 11-7 *Renaming the room tag*

Figure 11-8 *The renamed room tag*

8. Repeat steps 5 to 7 to add and rename the room tags of the other rooms in the first floor plan in the sequence of the room tag numbers shown in the sketch plan. Also, refer to the sketch, as shown in Figure 11-4, to name the respective rooms. Press the ESC Key to exit the tool.

Note
Depending on the view scale, the text height and other parameters of the room tag are automatically calculated by Autodesk Revit.

9. The completed room tags on the first floor level are shown in Figure 11-9.

Figure 11-9 The room tags added to all rooms in the first floor plan view

Adding Furniture Tags

In this section of the tutorial, you will use the **Tag** tool to add tags to the furniture items. The furniture tags were not loaded into this project file initially. Therefore, when you select a furniture item, Autodesk Revit prompts you to load the furniture tag from its library. You can load the furniture tag and then add tags to the items. You can also set the properties of the leader as specified in the project parameters. The added tags can then be suitably renamed.

1. Choose the **Annotate** tab and then choose the **Tag by Category** tool from the **Tag** panel.

2. Move the cursor over the bed in the bedroom and click when it is highlighted.

   On doing so, the **No Tag Loaded** dialog box is displayed informing that no tag is loaded for the element type selected and prompts you to load the tag.

3. In the message box, choose the **Yes** button; the **Load Family** dialog box is displayed.

4. Browse to the **Annotations > Architectural** folder and select **Furniture Tag** from the list of family files.

5. Choose the **Open** button to load the furniture tag.

6. Move the cursor over the bed and click when the furniture tag is displayed at an appropriate location; the furniture tag is added without a name and a "?" symbol, as shown in Figure 11-10.

7. Press ESC twice and select the furniture tag added in the previous step. On doing so, the **Modify | Furniture Tags** tab is displayed.

8. From the **Type Selector** drop-down list, select **Furniture Tag: Standard** to replace the boxed tag with a standard furniture tag without a box, as given in the project parameters.

9. Next, click on the tag name marked **?** to display the edit box and enter the name **Double Bed** in it, as specified in Figure 11-11. Next, press ENTER; Autodesk Revit displays a message box informing that you are changing a type parameter and it could affect many elements.

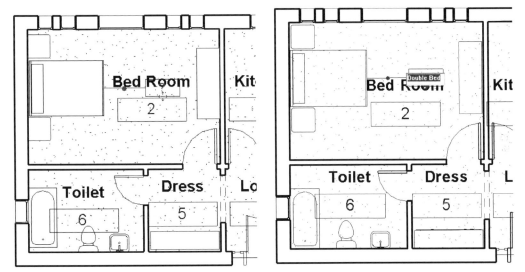

Figure 11-10 Using the *Tag* tool to add a furniture tag

Figure 11-11 Renaming the furniture tag

10. Choose **Yes** in the message box; the furniture tag is renamed.

    Next, you need to add an arrowhead to the furniture tag leader as per the parameters given.

11. Choose the **Edit Type** button from the **Properties** palette; the **Type Properties** dialog box is displayed.

12. Click in the **Value** column for the **Leader Arrowhead** parameter and select **Arrow 30 Degree** from the drop-down list.

13. Choose **Apply** and then **OK**; the **Type Properties** dialog box closes and the arrowhead is added to the furniture tag leader.

14. Drag the furniture tag upward to the new location using the move control, as shown in Figure 11-12.

15. Drag the leader elbow control represented by the blue dot upward in such a way that the leader appears similar to that shown in Figure 11-13.

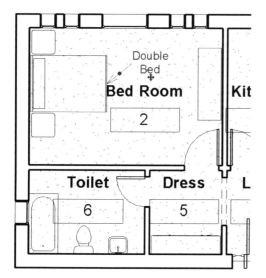

Figure 11-12 *Dragging the furniture tag to a new location*

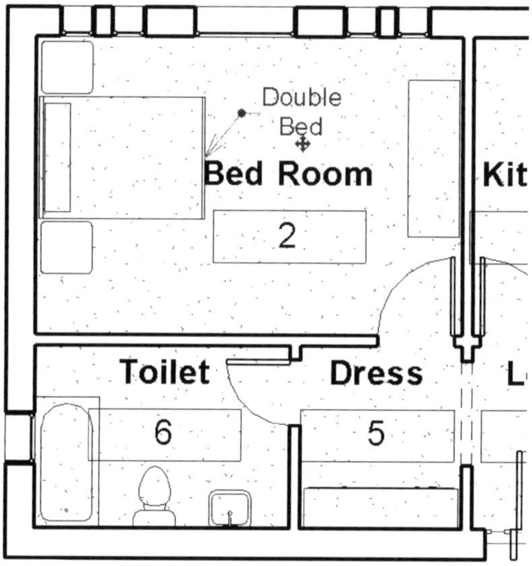

Figure 11-13 *Adjusting the tag leader at the new tag location*

16. Similarly, add other furniture tags to various furniture items in the **First Floor** plan view based on the given sketch plan, refer to Figure 11-13.

Invoking the Dimension Tool and Setting the Dimension Parameters

In this section of the tutorial, you will add dimensions to the project view. Note that the sketch plan shows two types of linear dimensions, centerline and wall faces. You will select appropriate dimension type from the **Type Selector** drop-down list. Further, you will use the **Type Properties** dialog box to create a new dimension style and set the parameters for the new dimension type as specified in the project parameters.

1. Start dimensioning the project view.

   Invoke the **Aligned** tool from the **Dimension** panel of the **Annotate** tab; the **Modify | Place Dimensions** tab is displayed.

2. Select the required dimension style from the **Type Selector** drop-down list.
   For Imperial   **Linear Dimension Style: Linear w Centre - 3/32" Arial**
   For Metric   **Linear Dimension Style: Diagonal_Centre - 2.5mm Arial**

3. Choose the **Edit Type** button from the **Properties** palette; the **Type Properties** dialog box is displayed.

4. Choose the **Duplicate** button to display the **Name** dialog box.

5. Enter **Linear Dimension - CL** in the **Name** edit box and choose the **OK** button.

6. Click in the **Value** column corresponding to the **Tick Mark** type parameter and select **Dot Filled 1/16" (Filled Dot 3mm)** from the drop-down list as specified in the project parameters.

7. Click in the **Value** column corresponding to the **Witness Line Gap to Element** type parameter and enter the value **1/4"(6 mm)**.

8. Choose the **Apply** button and then the **OK** button to close the **Type Properties** dialog box.

9. Repeat steps 2 to 5 to create another dimension style using the **Linear Dimension Style: Linear - 3/32" Arial (Linear Dimension Style: Diagonal - 2.5mm Arial** for Metric) and rename it to **Linear Dimension - Faces**. Modify the **Tick Mark** and **Witness Line Gap to Element** parameters to the values used for the **Linear Dimension - CL** dimension style.

Adding Dimensions to the Project View

Now, add dimensions to the project plan. As all the dimensions to be added are linear dimensions, use the **Linear** option to create them. In the following steps, you will add dimensions to the project plan using different methods. First, you will create centerline dimensions on the right and topsides of the plan view using the **Wall centerline** and **Individual References** options. Next, you will use the **Wall faces** and **Entire Walls** options to create interior dimensions of various rooms placed on the left and bottom of the plan view.

1. Select **Linear Dimension - CL** from the **Type Selector** drop-down list.

2. Ensure that the **Wall centerlines** option is selected from the drop-down list displayed in the **Options Bar**, and **Individual References** is selected in the **Pick** drop-down list.

3. Move the cursor over the south wall near the right corner of the plan view until the object snap for the wall centerline is highlighted, as shown in Figure 11-14. Click to start the dimension.

4. Move the cursor vertically upward until the object snap for the centerline of the north wall is displayed. Now, click to specify the endpoint of the dimension distance; the dimension line is displayed and the dimension moves with the cursor, as shown in Figure 11-15.

Figure 11-14 *Selecting the wall centerline reference to start a dimension*

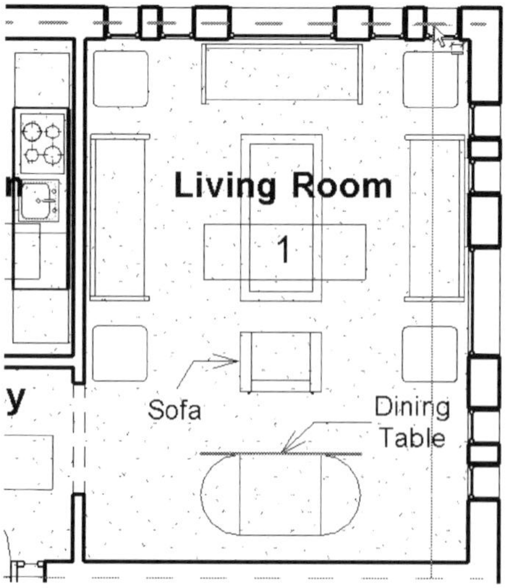

Figure 11-15 *Selecting the second wall centerline reference*

5. Move the cursor toward the right until it crosses the exterior wall and click to specify the location of the dimension. The dimension is created and its controls are highlighted, as shown in Figure 11-16.

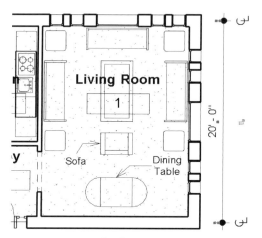

Figure 11-16 *The dimension with its controls*

6. To add dimensions to the north wall.

   Choose the **Entire Walls** option from the **Pick** drop-down list in the **Options Bar**.

7. Move the cursor over the north wall and click when it is highlighted.

   Autodesk Revit automatically selects the centerlines of the end walls and displays the dimension.

8. Move the cursor such that the dimension appears above the north wall, as shown in Figure 11-17, and click to place the dimension.

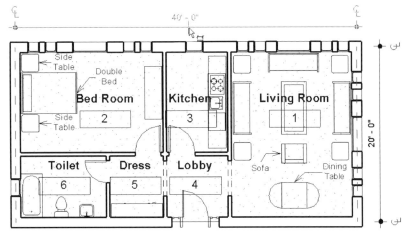

Figure 11-17 *Adding dimensions to the North wall*

9. Select the **Wall faces** option from the drop-down list on the left of the **Options Bar**.

10. Choose the **Options** button in the **Options Bar** to display the **Auto Dimension Options** dialog box.

11. Select the **Intersecting Walls** check box and choose the **OK** button.

12. Move the cursor over the west wall and click when it is highlighted; the dimensions are displayed.

13. Move the cursor such that the dimensions appear on the left side of the west wall and click to add them, as shown in Figure 11-18.

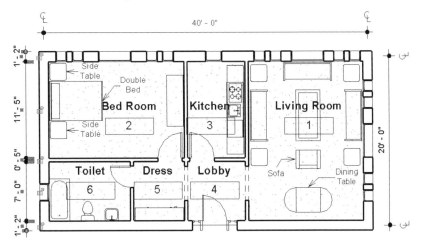

Figure 11-18 *Dimensions added to the West wall*

14. Using the above settings, add dimensions to the south wall.

15. Choose the **Modify** button from the **Select** panel of the **Modify | Place dimensions** contextual tab to exit the tool.

Saving the Project

In this section, you will save the project file using the **Save As** tool.

1. Choose **Save As > Project** from the **File** menu; the **Save As** dialog box is displayed. Enter **c11_Apartment1_tut1 (M_c11_Apartment1_tut1)** in the **File name** edit box and then choose **Save**.

2. Choose **Close** from the **File** menu to close the project file.

The completed *Apartment 1* plan view appears similar to the sketch plan given for this tutorial.

EXERCISES

Exercise 1   Club

Add rooms (without tags), room tags, and dimensions (linear, radial, and angular) to the first floor plan view of the *Club* project created in Tutorial 2 of Chapter 8, based on the sketch plan shown in Figure 11-19. Use the **Room Separator** tool to demarcate and tag the entrance lounge and passages. Note that dimensions for the east side hall are referenced to the wall centerlines, while those for the west hall are referenced to the wall faces. You can provide suitable names to the modified dimension styles. Ensure that the scale for the first floor plan view is set to 1/16"=1'0" (1: 200). The exact location of the room tags and dimensions is not important for this exercise. Use the following parameters for creating room tags and dimensions.

(Expected time: 30 min)

1. Room Tags:
   Room Tag with Area
2. Dimension Parameters:
For Imperial	Tick Mark- **Arrow Filled 30 Degree**
	Witness Line Gap to Element- **1/8"**
	Text Size- **1/8"**
	Text Offset- **1/16"**
For Metric	Tick Mark- **Arrow Filled 30 Degree**
	Witness Line Gap to Element- **3mm**
	Text Size- **3mm**
	Text Offset- **6mm**
3. Name of the file to be saved-
For Imperial	**c11_Club_ex1**
For Metric	**M_c11_Club_ex1**

Note

Dimensions and area values may deviate slightly from the one shown in the sketch plan.

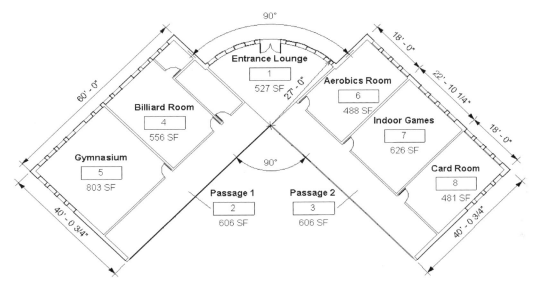

Figure 11-19 Sketch plan for adding room tags and dimensions to the Club project

Exercise 2   Elevator and Stair Lobby

Add text and dimensions to the first floor plan view of the *Elevator and Stairs Lobby* project created in Tutorial 3 of Chapter 8. Figure 11-20 shows partial first floor sketch plan of the project. The dimensions are to be added symmetrically on both sides of the vertical axis. Ensure that the view plan scale is set to 1/8"=1'0 (1: 400). All dimensions have wall centerlines as the reference. The exact location of the tags and dimensions is not important for this exercise. Use the following parameters for creating the dimensions.

(Expected time: 30 min)

1. Dimension Parameters:

    For Imperial   Dimension type to be based on: **Linear w Center 3/32" Arial**

    New dimension type name- **Linear 3/32" Arial-Stairs**

    Tick Mark- **Diagonal 1/8"**

    Witness Line Gap to Element- **1/8"**

    For Metric   Dimension type to be based on: **Diagonal Center 2.5 mm Arial**

    New dimension type name- **Linear 2.5 mm Arial-Stairs**

    Tick Mark- **Diagonal 3mm**

    Witness Line Gap to Element- **3mm**

2. Name of the file to be saved-

    For Imperial   **c11_ElevatorandStairLobby_ex2**

    For Metric   **M_c11_ElevatorandStairLobby_ex2**

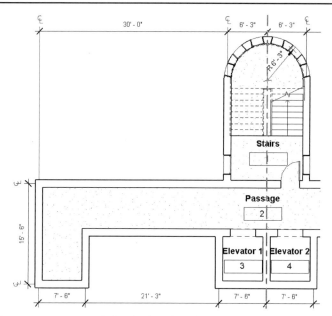

Figure 11-20 *Partial sketch plan for adding text and dimensions to the Elevator and Stair Lobby project*

Chapter *12*

Creating Project Details and Schedules

Learning Objectives

After completing this chapter, you will be able to:
- *Create a callout view*
- *Add crop region to the model*
- *Create a drafting detail*
- *Add text notes to the project detail*
- *Add model text to a building model*
- *Add revision cloud and revision tag to the project detail*
- *Create project schedules*

CREATING DETAILS IN A PROJECT

This method uses an enlarged portion of a building model view to create the project detailing. You can create a callout view by using plan, section, elevation, or detail view as its parent view. A new view is added to the **Project Browser** and is displayed under the same head as the parent view. The callout view is dependent on its parent view and is deleted if the parent view is deleted.

You can then sketch detail lines over the callout view to create the detail. Autodesk Revit provides various in-built detail components that can also be added to the detail view. In addition to this, while detailing you can crop views, sketch boundaries, and fill the sketched boundary with required filling material. Also, you can add break lines, dimensions, and annotations to the detailed views. The various tools and methods to create detailed views are discussed next.

Callout View

A callout view is used to display an enlarged view of a part of a building model. This view is important for detailing. Creating a callout view is a common practice amongst engineers as it helps them to view the project more precisely and with a higher detail. In an architectural project, callout is used to show details of the basic building elements in a model. You can create callout in plan view or in elevation view. Note that, the callout tag added to these views will be linked to the callout view.

A callout tag consists of the following parts: callout bubble, callout head, and leader line, as shown in Figure 12-1. The callout bubble is the line drawn around that part of the model that you want to enlarge. The callout head is the symbol that represents the callout displaying detail number and sheet number of a model. The line connecting the callout bubble to the callout head is called the leader line.

You can create callout views either by sketching or by creating a rectangle. The methods of creating and displaying callout view, modifying callout view properties, and adding detail lines to a callout view are discussed in the next section.

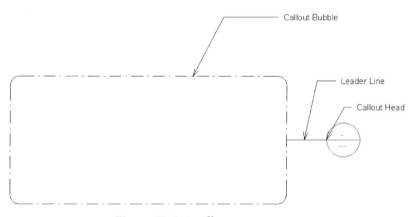

Figure 12-1 *A callout tag*

Adding Details to the Callout View

Autodesk Revit provides various tools to add details to a callout view. In the callout view, you can sketch lines using the **Detail Line** tool and add the detail components provided in the Autodesk Revit's library.

Detail Lines
Filled Region
Detail Components
Insulation Barrier
Break Line
Text Notes
Adding Detail Lines

CREATING DRAFTED DETAILS

Drafted details are created for the details that are not referenced to the existing project views. These details are not linked to a building model, therefore, they do not get updated with it. To create a drafted detail, first create a drafting view and then use the drafting tools provided in Autodesk Revit to sketch the detail. You can also import in-built details from Autodesk Revit's detail library and use them. The created drafted detail can then be used as a reference detail.

ADDING TEXT NOTES

Text notes form an important part of a project detail. They not only help in adding the specification for various building elements but also help in conveying the specific design intent. Autodesk Revit provides a variety of options to add text notes to a building model detail view by using the **Text** tool.

Revision Clouds

While creating project plans, you may need to revise a portion of a project view and issue the revised drawings to the concerned authorities. The revision cloud is added to refer and to indicate the revised portion. Except 3D views, you can add the revision cloud to any project view such as floor plans, elevations, sections, and so on. Autodesk Revit enables you to create the revision clouds of the desired shape and size. You can also add a revision tag to the revision cloud for referring to the revisions made to a specified area.

USING SCHEDULES IN A PROJECT

Schedule is another format for providing project information. In a building project, there may be different items that can be used a number of times at different locations. Schedules are primarily used to provide information regarding these items in a tabulated form. For each item, the schedule tables provide information regarding its size, material, cost, finish, level, and so on. These schedules can then be used by associated agencies for various purposes. They can assist the fabricating agency to manufacture all such items. The quantity surveyors and estimators can calculate the quantity and cost of the grouped items.

TUTORIALS

Tutorial 1   Apartment 1 - Callout View

In this tutorial, you will create a callout view of the kitchen door jamb in the *Apartment 1* project represented by a highlighted rectangle with a cursor, as shown in Figure 12-2. You will use the *c11_Apartment1_tut1.rvt* file created in Tutorial 1 of Chapter 11. You need to add the detail lines, detail components, text notes, and break lines to complete the door jamb detail, as shown in Figure 12-3. Use the parameters given in the figure and those given below to create it.

(Expected time: 1hr)

1. Callout view parameters:
    Callout view name to be assigned- **Door Jamb Detail**
    View Scale- **1 1/2" = 1'-0"**   View Scale- **1:10 (For Metric)**
    Detail Level- **Fine**

2. Detail component to be loaded from the **US Imperial > Detail Items (Detail Components) > Div 06-Wood and Plastic > 061100-Wood Framing** and **US Imperial > Detail Items (Detail Components) >Div 08-Openings > 081400-Wood Doors** folder locations.

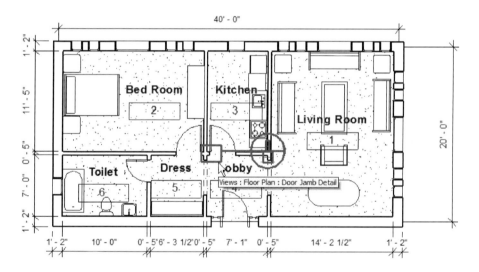

Figure 12-2 *Sketch plan for adding a callout view to the Apartment 1 project plan*

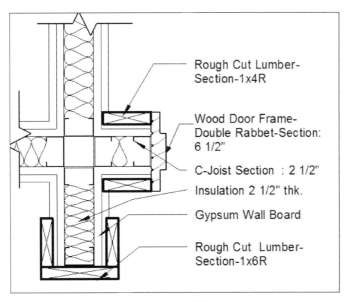

Rough Cut Lumber-Section-1x4R

Wood Door Frame-Double Rabbet-Section: 6 1/2"

C-Joist Section : 2 1/2"

Insulation 2 1/2" thk.

Gypsum Wall Board

Rough Cut Lumber-Section-1x6R

Figure 12-3 The callout view of the Apartment 1 project

3. Insulation instance parameters:
   Insulation Width: **2 1/2" (64 mm)**
   Insulation Bulge to Width Ratio: **3**

4. Text note parameters:
   Text Size: **3/32" (2.4 mm)**
   Leader Arrowhead: **Arrow Filled 15 - Degree**

5. Load the break line from **US Imperial > Detail Items (Detail Components)** folder (For Metric **US Metric > Detail Items (Detail Components)** folder) with the following modified parameters:
   Values for the **Right** and **Left** instance parameter: **0' 4" (102 mm)**
   Values for the **Jag Depth**, **Jag Width**, and **Masking depth** parameters: **0' 2" (51 mm)**

   The following steps are required to complete this tutorial:

a. Open the specified project file and then create the callout view using the **Callout** tool, refer to Figure 12-4.
b. Display the view and set its parameters, refer to Figure 12-5.
c. Use the callout view as an underlay and add detail components using the **Detail Component** tool, refer to Figures 12-6 through 12-8.
d. Add detail lines to the callout view using the **Detail Lines** tool, refer to Figures 12-9 through 12-11.
e. Use the **Insulation** tool to add insulation to the detail, refer to Figures 12-12 and 12-13.
f. Invoke the **Text** tool and add the text notes after setting the parameters, refer to Figures 12-14 through 12-16.
g. Add break lines to complete the detail callout view.
h. Save the project using the **Save As** tool.

For Imperial   *c12_Apartment1_tut1.rvt*
For Metric   *M_c12_Apartment1_tut1.rvt*
i.   Close the project.

Opening the Project File and Creating the Callout View

1. To start a project, choose **Open > Project** from the **File** menu and open the *c11_Apartment_tut1.rvt* file created in Tutorial 1 of Chapter 11. The first floor plan is displayed. You can also download this file from *http://www.cadsofttech.com*. The path of the file is as follows: *Textbooks > Civil/GIS > Revit Architecture > Revit Architecture 2019 For Novices*

2. Choose the **Zoom in Region** tool from the **Navigation Bar** and zoom near the area inside the rectangle, refer to Figure 12-2.

3. Next, choose the **Rectangle** tool from the **View > Create > Callout** drop-down; the **Modify | Callout** tab is displayed.

4. Click at two points to define the callout view rectangle, as shown in Figure 12-4.

   The callout view created is displayed as **First Floor - Callout 1** under the **Floor Plans** head in the **Project Browser**.

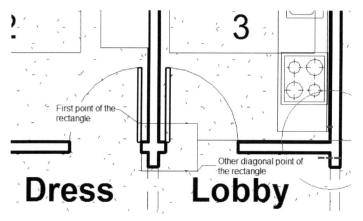

Figure 12-4 Defining the rectangle to create a callout view

Displaying the Callout View and Setting View Parameters

1. To display the callout view, double-click on the callout view name **First Floor- Callout 1** under the **Floor Plans** head in the **Project Browser**.

   Now, select the door element in the callout view and right-click; a shortcut menu is displayed. Choose **Hide in view > Category** from the shortcut menu; the doors in this view are now hidden, as shown in Figure 12-5.

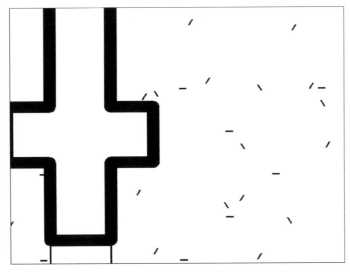

Figure 12-5 Callout view displayed in the viewing area

2. In the **Properties** palette, click in the **Value** field for the **View Name** instance parameter and enter **Door Jamb Detail**.

3. For the **View Scale** parameter, click in its value field and select the desired option from the corresponding drop-down list.
   For Imperial **1 1/2" = 1'- 0"**
   For Metric **1 : 10**

4. Similarly, click in the value fields for the **Display Model** and **Detail Level** parameters and then select **Halftone** and **Fine** from the corresponding drop-down lists.

Adding Detail Components

In this section of the tutorial, you will add detail components by using the callout view as an underlay. Further, you will load the desired components, place them at the required location, and then modify their sizes.

1. Choose the **Annotate** tab and then choose the **Detail Component** tool from the **Component** drop-down of the **Detail** panel; the **Modify | Place Detail Component** tab is displayed.

   Next, you need to load the components according to the project parameters.

2. Choose the **Load Family** tool from the **Mode** panel; the **Load Family** dialog box is displayed.

3. Navigate to **US Imperial > Detail Items > Div 08-Openings > 081400-Wood Doors** and select the **Wood Door Frame-Double Rabbet-Section** file (**US Metric > Detail Items >Div 08- Doors and Windows > 08200-Wood and Plastic Doors > 08210- Wood Doors** and select the **M_Wood Door Frame-Double Rabbet-Section** file). Now, choose **Open**; the selected file is loaded and it will be available in the **Type Selector** drop-down list.

4. Choose the **Type Properties** tool from the **Properties** panel; the **Type Properties** dialog box is displayed.

5. Choose **Duplicate**; the **Name** dialog box is displayed. Enter **6 1/2" (165 mm)** in the **Name** edit box and choose **OK**. Now, in the **Value** fields for the **Width** and **Stop** parameters, enter **0' 6 1/2" (165 mm)** and **0' 3" (76 mm)**, respectively.

6. Now, choose **OK**; the **Type Properties** dialog box will close.

7. Choose the **Load Family** tool from the **Mode** panel; the **Load Family** dialog box is displayed. In this dialog box, navigate to **US Imperial > Detail Items > Div 06-Wood and Plastic > 061100-Wood Framing** and select the **Rough Cut Lumber-Section** file (for Metric **US Metric > Detail Items > Div 06-Wood and Plastic > 06100- Rough Carpentry > 06110- Wood Framing** and select the **M_Rough Cut Lumber-Section** file). Next, choose **Open**; the **Specify Types** dialog box is displayed.

8. Choose **1x4R** and **1x6R** (for metric **25x100mm** and **25x165mm**) in the **Type** column using the CTRL key and then choose **OK**; the **Specify Types** dialog box will close and the selected types will now be available in the **Type Selector** drop-down list in the **Properties** palette.

 Note

*You can create the others sizes of the sections by chossing the **Duplicate** button from the **Type Properties** dialog box.*

9. From the **Type Selector** drop-down list, select **Wood Door Frame-Double Rabbet-Section: 6 1/2" (165 mm)**.

10. Select the **Rotate after placement** check box available in the **Options Bar**.

11. Move the cursor to the viewing area and click near the door jamb location to place the door frame. Rotate it 90 degrees in counterclockwise direction to achieve the correct orientation and then click again. Next, choose the **Modify** button from the **Select** panel. Then, select the placed door frame and use the **Move** tool and the **Midpoint** snap option to move the door frame to the location shown in Figure 12-6. Choose the **Modify** button from the **Select** panel.

12. Similarly, using the **Detail Component** tool and the editing tools, place the **Rough Cut Lumber-Section : 1x4R** component at the locations shown in Figure 12-7.

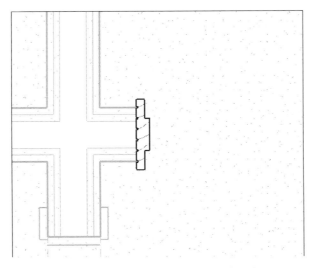

Figure 12-6 *Adding the door frame as a detail component*

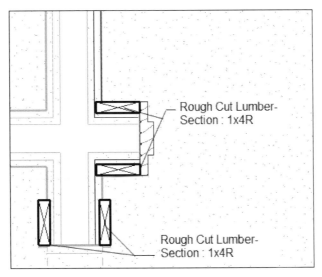

Figure 12-7 *Adding the wood board as a detail component*

You need to place another wood board of **6 1/2"** (165 mm) length. You can select and modify the properties of a similar component to create a new one.

13. Next, invoke the **Detail Component** tool and select the **Rough Cut Lumber-Section : 1x6R** option from the **Type Selector** drop-down list.

14. Choose the **Edit Type** button from the **Properties** palette; the **Type Properties** dialog box is displayed.

15. Choose the **Duplicate** button; the **Name** dialog box is displayed. Enter **1x 6.5R** in the **Name** edit box.

16. In the **Type Properties** dialog box, enter the value **0' 6 1/2" (165 mm)** in the **Value** column for the **Depth** dimension parameter.

17. Choose **OK**; the **Type Properties** dialog box is closed.

18. Ensure that the detail component **Rough Cut Lumber-Section : 1x6.5R** is selected in the **Type Selector** drop-down list and place it at the location, as shown in Figure 12-8.

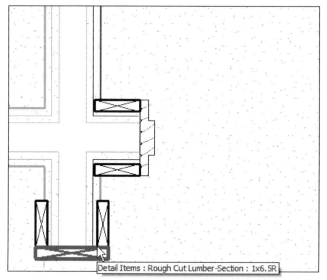

Figure 12-8 The modified wood board added as a detail component

Adding Detail Lines to the Project Detail

1. Choose the **Detail Line** tool from the **Detail** panel of the **Annotate** tab; the **Modify | Place Detail Lines** tab is displayed.

2. Ensure that the **Thin Lines** option is selected in the **Line Style** drop-down list in the **Line Style** panel. Now, use the snap options to sketch thin lines at 5/8" distance, depicting the double layer gypsum wall board in the callout view. You can also use the **Mirror**, **Offset**, and **Copy** tools to create detail lines. After adding the thin lines, the detail view will appear similar to the graphic shown in Figure 12-9.

3. After you create the details lines, you will add metal studs to support the gypsum boards. To do so, choose the **Detail Component** tool from **Annotate > Detail > Component** drop-down; the **Modify | Place Detail Component** tab is displayed.

4. Choose the **Load Family** tool from the **Mode** panel; the **Load Family** dialog box is displayed. Now, browse to the **US Imperial > Detail Items > Div 05-Metals > 054200-Cold-Formed Metal Joist Framing** folder and select the **C Joist-Section** file (for Metric **US Metric > Detail Items > Div 05-Metals > 05400-Cold-Formed Metal Framing > 05420-Cold-Formed Metal Joists** folder and select the **M_C Joist-Section** file). Now, choose **Open**; the selected file will now be loaded and can be selected from the **Type Selector** drop-down list.

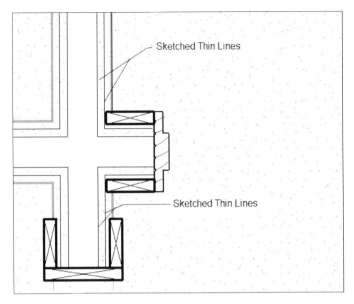

Figure 12-9 *The detail lines added to the callout view*

5   Ensure that the **C Joist-Section : 5 1/2"** (**140mm**)is selected in the **Type Selector** drop-down list and then choose the **Edit Type** button from the **Properties** palette; the **Type Properties** dialog box is displayed.

6.   Choose **Duplicate**; the **Name** dialog box is displayed. Enter **2 1/2" (64 mm)** in the **Name** edit box and then choose **OK** to close the **Name** dialog box.

7.   Now, in the **Type Properties** dialog box, click in the **Value** fields of the **Width** and **Depth** parameters and enter **2 1/2" (64 mm)** and **1 1/2" (38 mm)**, respectively.

8.   Choose **OK**; the **Type Properties** dialog box closes and the new type of joist section is selected in the **Type Selector** drop-down list.

9.   Move the cursor in the drawing area and then use the editing tools to add the selected type of joist to the detail view, as shown in Figure 12-10.

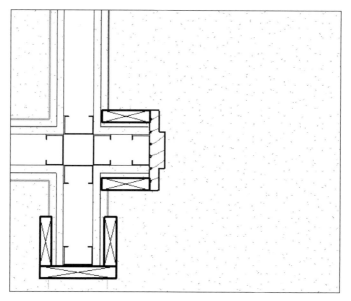

Figure 12-10 *The medium detail lines added to the detail view*

Adding an Insulation to the Detail

After you have added detail components and detail lines, you will add insulation between the metal joist framing members by using the **Insulation** tool.

1. To add insulation, choose the **Insulation** tool from the **Detail** panel of the **Annotate** tab; the **Modify | Place Insulation** tab is displayed.

2. Ensure that the **Line** tool is chosen in the **Draw** panel. Next, enter **0' 2 1/2" (64 mm)** in the **Width** edit box and choose **to near side** from the drop-down list in the **Option bar**.

3. Move the cursor to the drawing window and click to specify the location of the start point and end point of the insulation, as shown in Figure 12-11. Now, press ESC twice; the insulation is created.

4. Next, select the insulation that you have recently created; the **Modify | Insulation Batting Lines** tab is displayed.

5. In the **Properties** palette, click in the value column of the **Insulation Bulge to Width Ratio (1/x)** parameter and enter **3**. Now, choose **Apply**; the type property of the selected component gets modified.

6. Similarly, to add other insulations, repeat steps 1 to 5 of this section. refer to Figure 12-12 for location.

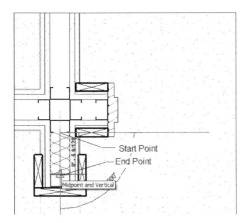

Figure 12-11 Sketching the insulation

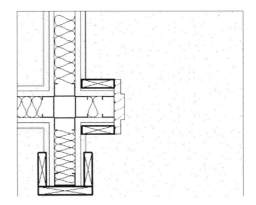

Figure 12-12 The insulations added to the detail view

Adding Text Notes to the Detail

You need to add text notes to the detail. Use an existing text note style as a template and create a new text type by modifying its parameters, as given in the project parameters.

1. Choose the **Text** tool from the **Text** panel of the **Annotate** tab; the **Modify | Place Text** tab is displayed.

2. From the **Type Selector** drop-down list, select **Text: 3/32" Arial (2.5mm Arial)**.

3. In the **Properties** palette, choose the **Edit Type** button; the **Type Properties** dialog box is displayed.

4. Choose **Duplicate** from the dialog box; the **Name** edit box is displayed.

5. Enter the name **Text Notes** in the **Name** edit box and choose **OK**.

6. In the **Type Properties** dialog box, ensure that the value for the **Text Size** type parameter is **3/32" (2.5 mm)**.

7. For the **Leader Arrowhead** parameter, select **Arrow Filled 15 Degree** from the drop-down list.

8. Choose **Apply** and **OK**; the settings are applied to the text notes and the **Type Properties** dialog box closes.

9. To add the text note with two segment leaders, choose the **Two Segments** tool from the **Leader** panel of the **Modify | Place Text** tab. If you want to create a text note with two segment leaders, you need to specify three points. The first point specifies the location of the leader head, the second point specifies the leader elbow, and the third point specifies the start point of the text.

10. Click on the door panel, refer to Figure 12-13, to specify the first point and move the cursor upward in the right direction and then click to specify the elbow point. Next, move the cursor horizontally toward right and click to specify the endpoint of the leader (start point of the text), as shown in Figure 12-13.

11. Enter the text **Wood Door Frame - Double Rabbet-Section**: **6 1/2** " (for Metric **Wood Door Frame - Double Rabbet-Section**: **165 mm**) in the edit box, as shown in Figure 12-14. Click outside the text box to complete the text note.

12. Similarly, add other text notes at appropriate locations, as shown in Figure 12-15, and press ESC when you have completed entering the text.

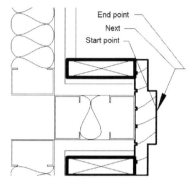

Figure 12-13 *Specifying three points for creating the text note with two segment leaders*

Figure 12-14 *Writing the text for the text note*

Adding Break Lines

In this section of the tutorial, you will add break line symbols to the continuing walls at the left and right by using the **Detail Component** tool.

1. Choose the **Detail Component** tool from **Annotate > Detail > Component** drop-down; the **Modify | Place Detail Component** tab is displayed.

2. Choose the **Load Family** tool from the **Mode** panel; the **Load Family** dialog box is displayed. Now, browse to **US Imperial/Metric > Detail Items (Detail Components) > Div 01 - General** folder and select the **Break Line** file. Choose **Open**; the **Load Family** dialog box closes, and the **Break Line** option gets selected in the **Type Selector** drop-down list.

3. Move the cursor in the drawing view and add the first break line horizontally at the top of the callout view, refer to Figure 12-15.

4. After you add the first break line, choose the **Modify** button from the **Select** panel and then select the break line you have recently added; the **Modify | Detail Items** tab is displayed.

5. In the **Properties** palette, click in the value fields of the **right** and **left** instance parameters and enter **0' 4"** **(102 mm)**.

6. Similarly, click in the value fields of the **Jag Depth**, **Jag Width**, and **Masking depth** parameters and enter **0' 2"** **(51 mm)**. Now, choose **Apply** so that the specified instance parameters are assigned to the selected break line. Next, you need to add a vertically aligned break line on the left of the callout view, refer to Figure 12-15.

7. Copy the first break line, place it at the specified location, and then rotate it. Use the **Copy** and **Rotate** tools to add this line.

8. In the **Project Browser**, click on the **Door Jamb Detail** sub-head under the **Floor Plans** head; the instance properties of the callout view are displayed in the **Properties** palette.

9. In the **Properties** palette, click in the value field of the **Display Model** instance parameter and select the **Do not display** option from the drop-down list to restrict the display of the building model. Next, choose the **Apply** button.

The completed tutorial resembles the detail sketch plan, as shown in Figure 12-15.

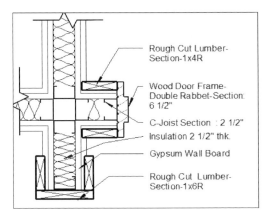

Figure 12-15 Text added to the callout detail

Saving the Project

In this section, you will save the project file using the **Save As** tool.

1. Now, choose **Save As > Project** from the **File** menu; the **Save As** dialog box is displayed. Enter **c12_Apartment1_tut1** (for Metric **M_c12_Apartment1_tut1**) and choose **Save**; the project file is now saved.

2. Now, close the project file by choosing **Close** from the **File** menu.

Tutorial 2	Apartment 1 - Schedules

In this tutorial, you will create the door, room, and wall schedule for the *Apartment 1* project, based on the schedule given in Figures 12-16, 12-17, and 12-18.   **(Expected time: 30 min)**

The following steps are required to complete this tutorial:

a. Open the project file and then invoke the **Schedule/Quantities** tool.
b. Set the schedule properties for creating a door schedule using the **Schedule Properties** dialog box, based on the schedules given.
c. Create the door schedule.
d. Set the schedule properties for creating the room schedule using the **Schedule Properties** dialog box based on the schedules given.
e. Create the room schedule.
f. Create the wall schedule.

g. Save the project using the **Save As** tool.
    For Imperial   *c12_Apartment1_tut2.rvt*
    For Metric   *M_c12_Apartment1_tut2.rvt*
h. Close the project.

Opening the Project File and Invoking the Schedule/Quantities Tool

1. Choose **Open > Project** from the **File** menu to open the *Apartment 1* project created in the previous tutorial. You can also download this file from *http://www.cadsofttech.com*. The path of the file is as follows: *Textbooks > Civil/GIS > Revit Architecture > Revit Architecture 2019 For Novices*.

2. Double-click on the **First Floor** under the **Floor Plans** head in the **Project Browser** to open the first floor plan.

3. Invoke the **Schedule/Quantities** tool from **View > Create > Schedules** drop-down; the **New Schedule** dialog box is displayed.

Setting the Parameters for the Door Schedule

1. In the **New Schedule** dialog box, choose **Doors** from the **Category** list and ensure that the **Schedule building components** radio button is selected. Choose the **OK** button; the **Schedule Properties** dialog box is displayed. You can now set the desired parameters based on the door schedule given in Figure 12-16.

Door Schedule				
Type Mark	Level	Width	Height	Count
4	First Floor	2' - 6"	7' - 0"	1
4	Fourth Floor	2' - 6"	7' - 0"	1
4	Second Floor	2' - 6"	7' - 0"	1
4	Third Floor	2' - 6"	7' - 0"	1
8	First Floor	3' - 0"	7' - 0"	1
8	First Floor	3' - 0"	7' - 0"	1
8	Fourth Floor	3' - 0"	7' - 0"	1
8	Fourth Floor	3' - 0"	7' - 0"	1
8	Second Floor	3' - 0"	7' - 0"	1
8	Second Floor	3' - 0"	7' - 0"	1
8	Third Floor	3' - 0"	7' - 0"	1
8	Third Floor	3' - 0"	7' - 0"	1
15	First Floor	3' - 0"	7' - 0"	1
15	Fourth Floor	3' - 0"	7' - 0"	1
15	Second Floor	3' - 0"	7' - 0"	1
15	Third Floor	3' - 0"	7' - 0"	1
Grand total: 16				

Figure 12-16 Door schedule for the Apartment 1 project

2. In the **Fields** tab, use the CTRL key and select **Count, Height, Level, Type Mark**, and **Width** from the **Available fields** list.

3. Choose the **Add parameter(s)** button to add these fields to the **Scheduled fields** list.

    The fields in the **Scheduled fields** list need to be arranged in the same order as they appear in the schedule. To do so, use the **Move parameter up** and **Move parameter down** buttons.

4. Select the **Type Mark** option in the **Scheduled fields** list and choose the **Move parameter up** button thrice to move this field to the top of the list.

5. Similarly, using the **Move parameter up** and **Move parameter down** buttons, arrange the other fields in the following order: **Level, Width, Height**, and **Count** after the **Type Mark** field.

    Notice that the door schedule to be created is arranged according to the type marks. For this reason, you need to use the **Sorting/Grouping** tab to create this sorting.

6. In the **Schedule Properties** dialog box, choose the **Sorting/Grouping** tab to display its contents.

7. Select the **Type Mark** option from the **Sort by** drop-down list.

8. Select the **Grand totals** check box to generate the total count.

9. Choose the **OK** button to close the **Schedule Properties** dialog box.

    Autodesk Revit displays the created schedule in the drawing window, refer to Figure 12-17. The **Door Schedule** is added under the **Schedules/Quantities** head in the **Project Browser**.

Setting the Parameters for the Room Schedule

1. Choose the **View** tab and then invoke the **Schedule/Quantities** tool from the **Schedules** drop-down in the **Create** panel; the **New Schedule** dialog box is displayed.

2. Choose **Rooms** from the **Category** list and choose the **OK** button; the **Schedule Properties** dialog box is displayed. You will use this dialog box to set the desired room schedule parameters.

3. Hold the CTRL key and select **Area, Level, Name, Number**, and **Perimeter** from the **Available fields** list in the **Fields** tab.

4. Choose the **Add parameter(s)** button to add these fields to the **Scheduled fields** list.

5. Using the **Move parameter up** and **Move parameter down** buttons, arrange the fields in the following order: **Name**, **Number**, **Level**, **Area**, and **Perimeter**.

6. Choose the **Sorting/Grouping** tab to display its contents.

7. Select the **Number** option from the **Sort by** drop-down list and select the **Grand totals** check box.

Note

*The total area of the room is shown in Figure 12-18. Now, use the **Formatting** tab to calculate the total area.*

8. Choose the **Formatting** tab to display its contents.

9. Select **Area** from the **Fields** list and then select the **Calculate totals** from the drop-down list displayed and ensure that the **Show conditional format on sheets** check box is selected.

10. Choose the **OK** button to close the **Schedule Properties** dialog box.

Autodesk Revit displays the Room Schedule in the drawing window, refer to Figure 12-17. Its name is added under the **Schedules/Quantities** head in the **Project Browser**.

Room Schedule				
Name	Number	Level	Area	Perimeter
Living Room	1	First Floor	268 SF	66' - 1 1/2"
Bed Room	2	First Floor	191 SF	56' - 3 1/2"
Kitchen	3	First Floor	81 SF	37' - 0 1/2"
Lobby	4	First Floor	50 SF	28' - 2"
Dress	5	First Floor	44 SF	26' - 7"
Toilet	6	First Floor	70 SF	34' - 0"
Grand total: 6			703 SF	

Figure 12-17 Room schedule for the Apartment 1 project

Setting the Parameters for the Wall Schedule

1. Choose the **View** tab and then invoke the **Schedule/Quantities** tool from the **Schedules** drop-down in the **Create** panel; the **New Schedule** dialog box is displayed.

2. Now, choose **Walls** from the **Category** list and choose the **OK** button; the **Schedule Properties** dialog box is displayed.

3. In the **Fields** tab, press and hold the CTRL key and select **Area**, **Family**, **Length**, **Type**, and **Volume** from the **Available fields** list.

4. Choose the **Add parameter(s)** button to add these fields to the **Scheduled fields** list.

5. Arrange the other fields in the following order: **Family**, **Type**, **Length**, **Volume**, and **Area** using the **Move parameter up** and **Move parameter down** buttons.

6. In the **Sorting/Grouping** tab, select the **Type** option from the **Sort by** drop-down list and then select the **Grand totals** check box. Clear the **Itemize every instance** check box.

7. Choose the **Formatting** tab to display its contents.

8. Select **Area** from the **Fields** list and select the **Calculate totals** option from the drop-down list displayed.

9. Similarly, select the **Calculate totals** check box for the **Length** and **Volume** fields.

10. Choose the **OK** button to close the **Schedule Properties** dialog box.

    Autodesk Revit displays the wall schedule in the drawing window and its name is added under the **Schedules/Quantities** head in the **Project Browser**.

11. You can adjust the column width of the schedule to accommodate the text in the **Type** column using the dragging tool. The created wall schedule appears similar to the schedule given in Figure 12-18.

<Wall Schedule>				
A	B	C	D	E
Family	Type	Length	Volume	Area
Basic Wall	Exterior - Brick on Mtl. Stud	120' - 0"	5623.49 CF	4864 SF
Basic Wall	Interior - 5" Partition (2-hr)	291' - 2"	1285.54 CF	3085 SF
Grand total: 20		411' - 2"	6909.03 CF	7949 SF

Figure 12-18 Wall schedule for the Apartment 1 project

This completes the tutorial for creating the schedules for the *Apartment 1* project.

12. Double-click on **First Floor** under the **Floor Plans** head in the **Project Browser**.

Saving the Project

In this section, you will save the project file using the **Save As** tool.

1. Choose **Save As > Project** from the **File** menu; the **Save As** dialog box is displayed. Enter **c12_Apartment1_tut2** (for Metric **M_c12_Apartment1_tut2**) in the **File name** edit box and choose **Save**; the project file is saved.

2. Choose **Close** from the **File** menu to close the project file.

EXERCISES

Exercise 1   Club - Drafted Detail

In the *Club* project created in Exercise 1 of Chapter 11, create a drafted detail based on the sketch given in Figure 12-19. Load the required detail items (detail components). Use wide and thin lines to sketch the detail lines. Assume the parameters for adding text notes, dimensions, and break lines. The exact placement of the elements is not important for this exercise. Save the project file as *c12_Club_ex1.rvt* (for Metric *M_c12_Club_ex1.rvt*).

(Expected time: 30 min)

To add the Window jamb detail component in the Project, you need to download the *Window Jamb - Metal Fixed Flush.rfa* file from the website: *www.cadsofttech.com*

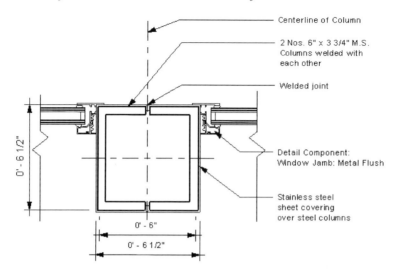

Figure 12-19 Sketch plan for creating a drafted detail for the Club project

Exercise 2   General- Sketch Detail

Create the drafted detail based on the sketch detail shown in Figure 12-20. Use the **Fill Region** tool to create elements and fill patterns. Assume the parameters for adding text notes and dimensions. The exact placement of the elements is not important for this exercise. Save the project file as *c12_sketchdetail_ex2.rvt* (for Metric *M_c12_sketchdetail_ex2.rvt)*

(Expected time: 30 min)

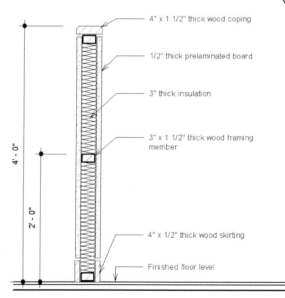

Figure 12-20 Sketch detail for creating a drafted detail

Chapter *13*

Creating and Plotting Drawing Sheets

Learning Objectives

After completing this chapter, you will be able to:

• *Add drawing sheets to a project*
• *Add views to a drawing sheet*
• *Print drawing sheets and project views*

CREATING DRAWING SHEETS

In Autodesk Revit, drawing sheets are treated like views in a project. They are defined by a border and a title block. Therefore, to create a drawing sheet, you first need to add a sheet view to the project.

Adding a Drawing Sheet to a Project

Ribbon: View > Sheet Composition > Sheet

To add a drawing sheet to a project, choose the **Sheet** tool from the **Sheet Composition** panel; the **New Sheet** dialog box will be displayed. This dialog box has two areas: **Select titleblocks** and **Select placeholder sheets**. Select the required title block for the drawing sheet from the list of title blocks. To load drawing sheets other than the ones in the list of title blocks in the **Select titleblocks** area, choose the **Load** button from the **New Sheet** dialog box; the **Load Family** dialog box will be displayed. Next, choose **US Imperial > Titleblocks** (for Metric **US Metric > Titleblocks**); the list of titleblocks family files will be displayed. Select the desired family file from the list to load it into your project and choose the **Open** button; the title block corresponding to the selected family file will be added to the list of title blocks in the **Select titleblocks** area. Select a titleblock from the list and choose the **OK** button; a titleblock of the selected family will be displayed in the drawing window, as shown in Figure 13-1.

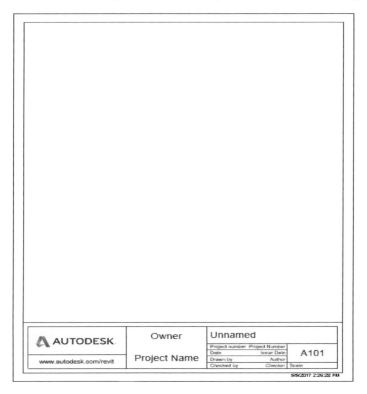

Figure 13-1 *Sheet view with the selected title block*

CREATING GUIDE GRIDS

Guide Grid is a customizable grid available in Revit sheets. It is used to place the drawing view in place in the sheet. To create a Guide Grid, choose the **Guide Grid** tool from the **Sheet Composition** panel of the **View** tab; the **Assign Guide Grid** dialog box will be displayed, as shown in Figure 13-2. In this dialog box, the **Create new** radio button is selected by default. You can enter a name for the Guide Grid in the **Name** edit box and choose the **OK** button; the Guide Grid will be displayed over the sheet in the drawing area, as shown in Figure 13-3. On creating a Guide Grid, it gets added as an instance property under the **Other** head in the **Properties** palette. Now, select the Guide Grid from the drawing area; the drag controls will be displayed. You can use the drag controls to resize the Guide Grids in the

*Figure 13-2 The **Assign Guide Grid** dialog box*

drawing area. The **Properties** palette displays the instance properties of the selected Guide Grid. In the **Properties** palette, you can specify guide spacing in the **Guide Spacing** edit box to increase or decrease the spacing of the grids. You can also rename the guide name under the identity data in the **Name** edit box in the **Properties** palette.

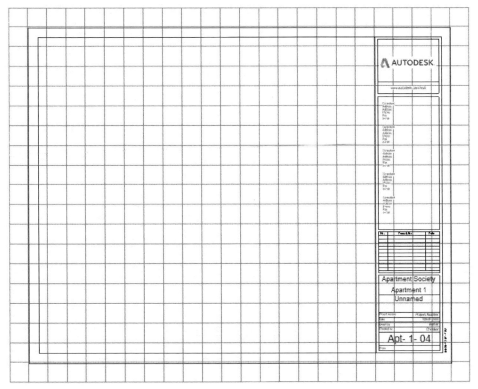

Figure 13-3 The Guide Grid displayed over the sheet

PRINTING IN Autodesk Revit

The created building model and project views can be stored in the computer's hard disk or on a temporary media. It also becomes imperative to print these views as a hard copy at various stages of the project. During the initial stages of the project development, you may need to print certain project views and discuss them with the others in your organization or with the clients. As the project progresses, other professional agencies such as structural, electrical, plumbing, HVAC, landscape, and so on become involved with the project. The printed drawings assist in a proper coordination between these agencies. The project may also require approval from statutory bodies and other departments. Printed drawings and project views explain the project and can be submitted as a complete set to obtain their approval.

TUTORIAL

Tutorial 1   Apartment 1

In this tutorial, you will create a drawing sheet for the *Apartment 1* project created in Tutorial 2 of Chapter 12, and then add the first floor plan, north elevation, longitudinal section, room schedule, and door schedule to the sheet, as shown in Figure 13-4. You will also add the following project and sheet information in the sheet title block:

(Expected time: 30 min)

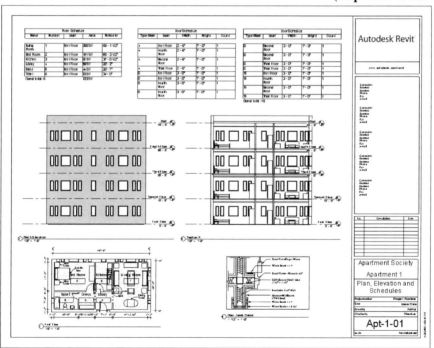

Figure 13-4 *Sheet layout for creating a drawing sheet for the Apartment 1 project*

1. Drawing sheet parameters:
    Titleblock to be used-
    >   For Imperial   **C17 x 22 Horizontal** from the **US Imperial > Titleblocks** folder.
    >   For Metric   **A2 metric** from the **US Metric > Titleblocks** folder.

2. Project information:
    Owner name: **Apartment Society**
    Project Name: **Apartment 1**
    Sheet name: **Plan, Elevation and Schedules**
    Sheet number: **Apt-1-01**

    The following steps are required to complete this tutorial:

a. Add a sheet by using the **New Sheet** tool and by loading the specified titleblock.
b. Add the project information to the sheet titleblock.
c. Add views to the sheet view and compose the drawing sheet.
d. Modify the visibility settings of the added views using the **Activate View** tool.
e. Add schedules to the sheet.
f. Edit schedules to compose them on the sheet.
g.   Save the project using the **Save As** tool.
    >   For Imperial   *c13_Apartment1_tut1.rvt*
    >   For Metric   *M_c13_Apartment1_tut1.rvt*
h. Close the project.

Adding a Sheet to the Project

First, you need to open the project file and create a new sheet view. You can load the titleblock from the specified folder.

1. Choose **Open > Project** from the **File** menu and open the *c12_Apartment1_tut2.rvt* (for Metric *M_c12_Apartment1_tut2.rvt*) file created in Tutorial 2 of Chapter 12. You can also download this file from *http://www.cadsofttech.com*. The path of the file is as follows: *Textbooks > Civil/GIS > Revit Architecture > Revit Architecture 2019 For Novices*

2. Choose the **Sheet** tool from the **Sheet Composition** panel in the **View** tab; the **New Sheet** dialog box is displayed.

3. Choose the **Load** button; the **Load Family** dialog box is displayed. In this dialog box, choose the titleblock **C 17 x 22 Horizontal** from **US Imperial > Titleblocks** folder (for Metric **A2 metric** from the **US Metric > Titleblocks** folder). On doing so, the specified titleblock is added to the list in the **Select titleblocks** area in the **New Sheet** dialog box.

4. Choose the **OK** button to close the **New Sheet** dialog box and create the sheet view by using the loaded titleblock.

Adding the Project Information to the Sheet Titleblock

In this section, you need to add the project information to the titleblock using the **Properties** palette. Further, you need to directly enter other project parameters in the title block.

1. Select the titleblock from the drawing window. Then, in the **Properties** palette, click in the value fields for the **Sheet Name** and **Sheet Number** parameters and enter **Plan, Elevation and Schedules** and **Apt-1-01**, respectively.

2. Choose **Apply**. You will notice that the values entered in the **Properties** palette are displayed in the sheet.

3. Next in the titleblock, click in the **Owner** field and enter **Apartment Society** in the edit box. Now, press ENTER to view the new value in the sheet.

4. Similarly, you need to click on the **Project Name** field in the titleblock in the drawing area and enter **Apartment 1** in the edit box and then press ENTER. Now, the project details appear in the titleblock, as shown in Figure 13-5.

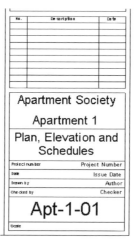

Figure 13-5 Project information in the titleblock of the sheet view

Adding Project Views to the Drawing Sheet

In this section, you need to add the specified project views by dragging their name from the **Project Browser** in the sheet. Further, you need to place the project views at their designated place in the sheet based on the sheet layout.

1. Drag **First Floor** from the **Floor Plans** head in the **Project Browser** into the drawing sheet. The view appears in the form of a rectangle in the sheet view.

2. Next, move the cursor to the lower left area of the titleblock such that the corner of the rectangle is close to the lower left corner of the drawing sheet. Next, click to place the view. The first floor plan view is added to the sheet and appears enclosed in a rectangle.

3. In the **Project Browser**, click on the **North** elevation node under the **Elevations (Building Elevation)** head and then right-click to display the shortcut menu. Choose the **Rename** option from the shortcut menu. In the **Name** edit box of this dialog box, enter **North Elevation** and then press ENTER to rename it.

4. Drag **North Elevation** and **Section X** from the **Project Browser** and add them to the specified locations in the sheet, refer to Figure 13-6. The three views are added to the sheet, as shown in Figure 13-6.

5. Next, drag the **Door Jamb Detail** view from the **Project Browser** and add it to the desired location in the sheet, refer to Figure 13-4.

Note
You may need to hide the annotations that are not needed to be viewed in the sheet.

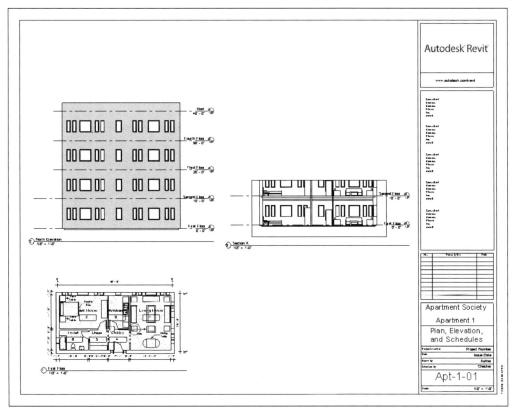

Figure 13-6 Project views added to the drawing sheet view

Modifying the Visibility of the Added Project Views

Notice that the project views in the drawing sheet given for this tutorial do not show the grids and section lines but show the complete section view. You can access each project view directly from the drawing sheet using the **Activate View** tool. Then, you can modify their visibility settings.

1. Select the **North Elevation** view from the drawing or highlight the view and then right-click to display the shortcut menu. Choose the **Activate View** option from the shortcut menu. On doing so, all the views except the selected one become grey. You can now use the editing tools to modify the building model and the visibility settings of the activated view.

2. Choose the **Visibility/ Graphics** tool from the **Graphics** panel in the **View** tab; the **Visibility/Graphic Overrides for Elevation: North Elevation** dialog box is displayed.

3. In the **Annotation Categories** tab, clear the check boxes for **Grids** and **Sections** in the **Visibility** column. Choose **OK** to close the dialog box and return to the drawing window.

4. Right-click in the drawing window, and then choose the **Deactivate View** option from the shortcut menu.

5. Repeat step 1 for activating the **Section X** view from the sheet. Next, repeat steps 2 and 3 to turn off the display of grids and sections in the activated view.

6. In the **Properties** palette for the **Section X** view, ensure that the check box corresponding to the **Crop Region Visible** parameter is selected. Next, in the sheet, select the boundary of the section view to display the view range controls.

7. Increase the size of the view range and display the entire section view by using the drag control located on the top as shown in the drawing sheet for this tutorial. You may use the **Zoom** tool to zoom in the section view. Next, right-click and choose **Deactivate View** from the shortcut menu.

Adding Schedules to the Drawing Sheet

Next, you need to add schedules to the drawing sheet in the same manner as you did in the case of the project view. Autodesk Revit, however, gives you the flexibility to divide larger schedules into smaller panels to accommodate them in the drawing sheet.

1. Drag **Room Schedule** from the **Schedules/Quantities** head in the **Project Browser**.

2. Move the cursor to the top left corner of the titleblock. The schedule is displayed and moves along with the cursor. Click to drop and add the room schedule at the location shown in the drawing sheet.

3. Similarly, drag and drop **Door Schedule** from the **Project Browser** to the drawing sheet. The door schedule is long and therefore you can use the **Split Schedule Table** tool to split it into two parts.

4. Click on the **Split Schedule Table** control available in the middle of the right edge of the door schedule, as shown in Figure 13-7. The schedule is divided into two parts and the second part is placed on the right of the first part, refer to Figure 13-4.

*Figure 13-7 Using the **Split Schedule Table** tool to split the table into two parts*

Saving the Project

In this section, you will save the project file using the **Save As** tool.

1. Choose **Save As > Project** from the **File** menu; the **Save As** dialog box is displayed. Enter **c13_Apartment1_tut1** (**M_c13_Apartment1_tut1** for Metric) in the **File name** edit box and then choose **Save**.

2. Next, choose **Close** from the **File** menu to close the project file.

EXERCISES

Exercise 1   Club

Create a drawing sheet for the *Club* project created in Exercise 3 of Chapter 12. Add the first floor and roof plan, north elevation, sections, and room schedule to the sheet, as shown in Figure 13-8. Use the following project and sheet information parameters:

(Expected time: 30 min)

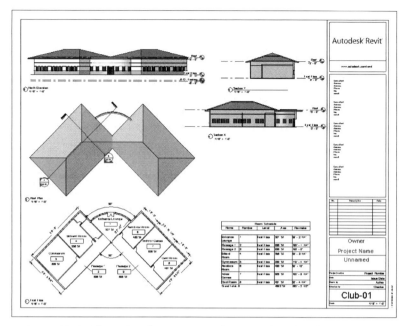

Figure 13-8 *Sheet view for creating a drawing sheet for the Club project*

1. Drawing sheet parameters:
    Title block to be used:

    For Imperial   **C 17 x 22 Horizontal** from **US Imperial > Titleblocks** folder.
    For Metric   **A2 metric** from **US Metric > Titleblocks** folder.

2. Project information:
    Owner name: **Club House**
    Sheet title: **Club Building**
    Sheet name: **Project Drawings**
    Sheet number: **Club-01**

3. Name of the file to be saved-
    For Imperial   **c13_Club_ex1**
    For Metric   **M_c13_Club_ex1**

 Note

The Club project has been created using the Commercial-Default.rte template and therefore it already contains various sheet views. Some of the views have already been placed in them. You need to create a copy of the views and then add them to the new sheet that you create. You may also need to modify the view scale.

Exercise 2   **Urban House**

Create a drawing sheet for the *i_Urban_House.rvt* project. You can download the *i_Urban_House.rvt* file from *http://www.cadsofttech.com*. The path of the file is as follows: *Textbooks > Civil/GIS > Revit Architecture >Revit Architecture 2019 For Novices*. In the drawing sheet, add the ground floor plan, first floor plan, second floor plan, south elevation, east elevation, and the 3D View 1, as shown in Figure 13-28. Use the titleblock **E1: 30 X 42 Horizontal** (for Metric **A0 metric** titleblock) for this exercise. All the views, except the 3D view, should be 1/8"=1'0"(for metric 1:100) view scale.

(Expected time: 30 min)

Save the file as:

| For Imperial | *c13_UrbanHouse_ex2.rvt* |
| For Metric | *M_c13_UrbanHouse_ex2.rvt* |

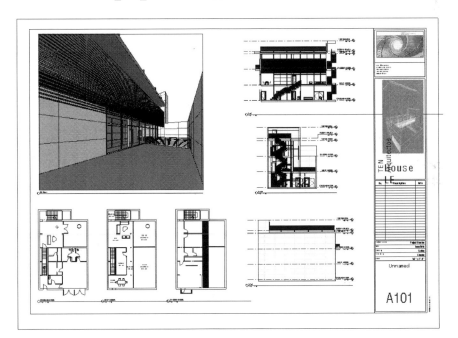

Figure 13-28 *Sheet view for creating a drawing sheet for the Urban House project*

This page is intentionally Left Blank

Chapter *14*

Creating 3D Views

Learning Objectives

After completing this chapter, you will be able to:

- *Generate orthographic view of a building model*
- *Use the Navigation tools to view a building model*
- *Generate perspective view using the Camera tool*
- *Modify the properties of perspective view*

THREE-DIMENSIONAL (3D) VIEWS

In Autodesk Revit, you can display a variety of three-dimensional (3D) views. There are two basic types of 3D views that can be created and viewed.

Orthographic View: An orthographic view is a 3D view of a building model in which all the elements are displayed in their actual sizes, irrespective of their distance from the source. This view is displayed automatically as a default 3D view. Once this view has been displayed, you can then use various tools to modify its properties.

Perspective View: A perspective view is displayed by placing a camera and specifying its eye elevation and target position.

Generating Orthographic View

Ribbon: View > Create > 3D View drop-down > Default 3D View

   In Autodesk Revit, the default 3D view is an orthographic view. To view a building model in orthographic projection, invoke the **Default 3D View** tool from the **Create** panel; the current view will change into the default 3D view.

   Note

*In Revit, there is no default {3D} view in the **Project Browser**. However, when you invoke the **Default 3D View** tool from the **Create** panel, the default {3D} view is added to the **Project Browser**.*

When you create an orthographic 3D view for the first time in a project, a camera is automatically placed at the default position (southeast corner) and the corresponding view is displayed in the drawing window. The default view is named as **{3D}** and is added under the **3D Views** head of the **Project Browser**. Figure 14-1 shows an example of the 3D view of a building model displayed using the **Default 3D View** tool.

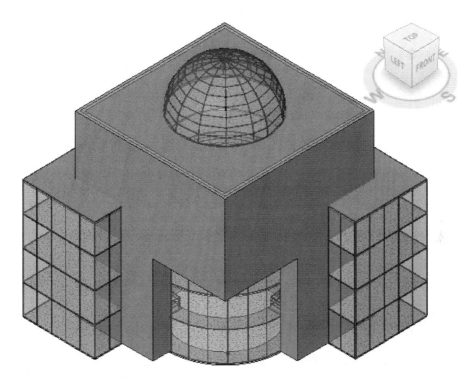

Figure 14-1 *3D view of a building model displayed using the **Default 3D View** tool*

TUTORIALS

Tutorial 1   Apartment 1

In this tutorial, you will create two interior perspective views for the first floor of the *Apartment 1* project created in Chapter 13 of this textbook, refer to Figures 14-2 and 14-3. The first figure shows the living room and the second figure shows the view of the lobby area from the living room. The exact view angle and height are not important for this tutorial.

(Expected time: 20 min)

Figure 14-2 *3D view of the living room for the Apartment 1 project*

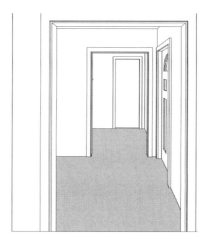

Figure 14-3 *3D view of the lobby area for the Apartment 1 project*

The following steps are required to complete this tutorial:
a. Open the project file and the ground floor plan view.
b. Generate the interior perspective view of the living room using the camera tool, refer to Figure 14-4 and Figure 14-5.
c. Generate the interior perspective view of the lobby room, refer to Figures 14-6 and 14-7.
d.   Save the project using the **Save As** tool.
       For Imperial   *c14_Apartment1_tut1.rvt*
       For Metric   *M_c14_Apartment1_tut1.rvt*
e. Close the project.

Opening the Project File and Invoking the Camera Tool

1. Choose **Open > Project** from the **File** menu and open the *c13_Apartment 1_tut1.rvt* file created in Tutorial 1 of Chapter 13. You can also download this file from *http://www.cadsofttech.com*. The path of the file is as follows: *Textbooks > Civil/GIS > Revit Architecture > Revit Architecture 2019 For Novices*.

2. Double-click on **First Floor** in the **Floor Plans** head of the **Project Browser** to open the corresponding floor plan in the drawing window.

3. Invoke the **Camera** tool from **View > Create > 3D View** drop-down; the **Options Bar** is displayed.

Generating the Interior Perspective View of the Living Room

In this section of the tutorial, you will specify the camera and the target points for the camera. You will use the default value **5'6"** (eye level) for both these points.

1. Select the **Perspective** check box in the **Options Bar**, if it is not selected by default.

2. Move the cursor to the lower right corner of the living room and click to specify the camera point.

3. Now, move the cursor toward the diagonally opposite ends of the living room and click when the field of view resembles the graphic shown in Figure 14-4. The drawing window shows the 3D interior view, as shown in Figure 14-5.

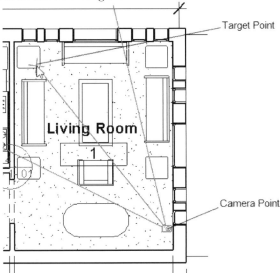

Figure 14-4 Specifying the camera point and the target point of the interior view

Figure 14-5 *The 3D interior view of the living room*

4. The selected 3D view shows the drag controls (blue dots at the midpoint of the four sides of the rectangle). Right-click in the drawing window and then choose **Zoom Out (2x)** from the shortcut menu.

5. Use the drag controls to increase the view extents based on the 3D view given for the living room. Next, press ESC to exit the **Modify | Cameras** tab.

6. In the **Project Browser**, right-click on **3D View 1** under **3D Views**; a shortcut menu is displayed. From the shortcut menu, choose the **Rename** option; an edit box is displayed. In the edit box, enter **Living Area**; the **3D View 1** view is renamed as **Living Area**.

Generating the Interior Perspective View of the Lobby

You can use similar steps to generate the 3D interior view of the lobby area.

1. Right-click on the **First Floor** view in the **Floor Plans** head in the **Project Browser** and choose **Open** from the shortcut menu to open the view.

2. Invoke the **Camera** tool from **View > Create > 3D View** drop-down. Ensure that the **Perspective** check box is selected in the **Options Bar** (default setting).

3. Move the cursor near the center of the opening between the lobby area and the living room, refer to Figure 14-6, and click to specify the camera point.

4. Move the cursor horizontally toward the left and click when the field of view resembles the graphic shown in Figure 14-6. The drawing window shows the 3D interior view of the lobby area, as shown in Figure 14-7.

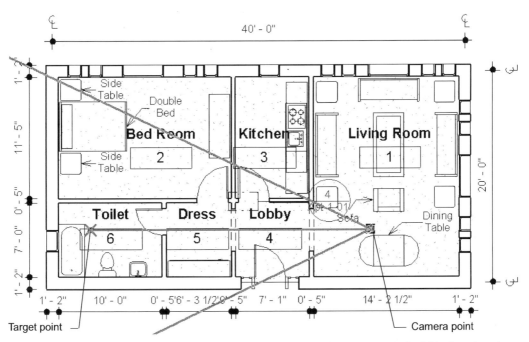

Figure 14-6 *Specifying the camera point and the target point for generating the lobby interior view*

5. Right-click in the drawing window and then choose **Zoom Out (2x)** from the shortcut menu displayed. Use the drag controls to increase the view extents.

6. Now, choose **Visual Style > Shaded** from the **View Control Bar**; the current view is shaded.

7. Use the drag controls to increase the view extents based on the 3D view given for the lobby area, refer to Figure 14-7.

8. Right-click on **3D View 1** in the **Project Browser** under **3D Views** and rename it as **Lobby Area** by using the **Rename** option from the shortcut menu.

Saving the Project

In this section, you will save the project file using the **Save As** tool.

1. Now, choose **Save As > Project** from the **File** menu; the **Save As** dialog box is displayed. Enter **c14_Apartment1_tut1** in the **File name** edit box and choose **Save**; the project file is saved.

2. Choose **Close** from the **File** menu to close the project file.

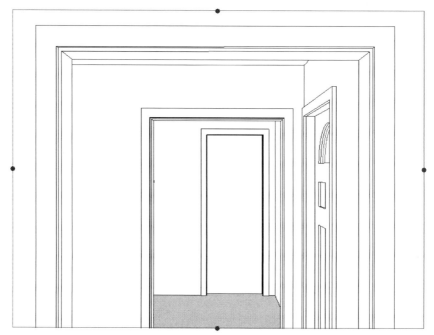

Figure 14-7 *The 3D interior view of the lobby area*

Tutorial 2   Club

Create an exterior 3D perspective view and an orthographic view for the *Club* project created in Exercise 1 of Chapter 13, refer to Figures 14-8 and 14-9. Note that the exterior 3D perspective view is from the main entrance. The exact view and height are not important for this tutorial.

(Expected time: 20 min)

The following steps are required to complete this tutorial:

a.   Open the project file and the First floor plan view.
b.   Invoke the **Camera** tool to generate the exterior 3D view.
c.   Generate the exterior perspective view of the Main Entrance, refer to Figure 14-10.
d.   Generate the orthographic view of the building, refer to Figure 14-12.
e.   Use the SteeringWheels and the **ORBIT** tool to display the orthographic view.
f.   Save the project using the **Save As** tool.

     For Imperial   *c14_Club_tut2.rvt*
     For Metric   *M_c14_Club_tut2.rvt*

g.   Close the project.

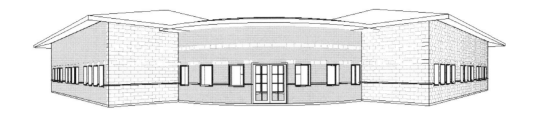

Figure 14-8 *3D exterior view of the main entrance of the club building*

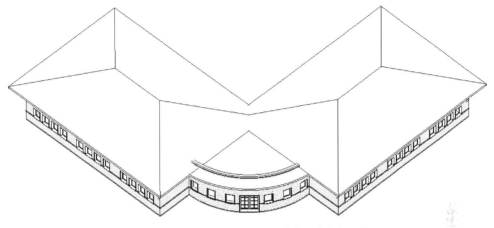

Figure 14-9 *Orthographic view of the Club building*

Opening the Project File and Invoking the Camera Tool

1. Choose **Open > Project** from the **File** menu and open the *c13_Club_ex1.rvt* file created in Exercise 1 of Chapter 13. You can also download this file from *http://www.cadsofttech.com*. The path of the file is as follows: *Textbooks > Civil/GIS > Revit Architecture > Revit Architecture 2019 For Novices*.

2. Double-click on **First Floor** in the **Floor Plans** head of the **Project Browser** to open the corresponding floor plan in the drawing window.

3. Invoke the **Camera** tool from **View > Create > 3D View** drop-down; the options for inserting the camera are displayed in the **Options Bar**.

Generating the Exterior Perspective View of the Main Entrance

You need to specify the camera and target points. Also, you will use the default value **5'6"** (**1650** mm) (eye level) for both these points.

1. Select the **Perspective** check box in the **Options** Bar if not selected by default.

2. Move the cursor vertically above the main entrance door and click to specify the camera point, as shown in Figure 14-10.

3. Move the cursor vertically downward and click when the field of view resembles the graphic shown in Figure 14-10; the drawing window shows the 3D exterior view of the main entrance, as shown in Figure 14-11.

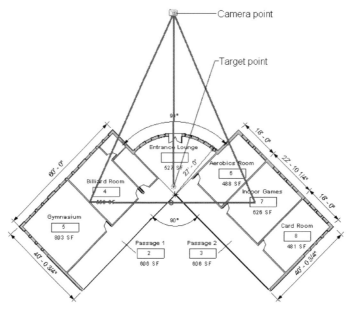

Figure 14-10 *Specifying the camera and the target points for the exterior view*

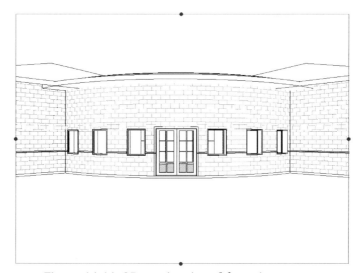

Figure 14-11 *3D exterior view of the main entrance*

4. Right-click in the drawing window and choose **Zoom Out (2x)** from the shortcut menu.

5. Ensure that the crop region of the 3D view is selected in the drawing and it displays the drag controls (blue dots at the midpoint of the four sides of the rectangle).

6. Use the drag controls to increase the view extents based on the 3D view given for the entrance view. Press ESC to exit the **Camera** tool.

7. Rename **3D View 1** to **Entrance View** by using the **Rename** option from the shortcut menu displayed on right-clicking in the view name in the **Project Browser**.

Generating the Orthographic View of the Club Building

You need to display the orthographic view of the club building using the SteeringWheels.

1. Invoke the **Default 3D View** tool from **View > Create > 3D View** drop-down.

2. Move the cursor toward the ViewCube and right-click on it; a shortcut menu is displayed.

3. Choose **Orient to a Direction > Northeast Isometric** from the shortcut menu; the northeast isometric view is displayed, as shown in Figure 14-12.

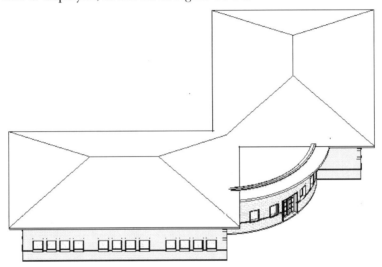

Figure 14-12 Northeast isometric view of the Club building

4. Press the F8 key to display SteeringWheels.

5. Next, press and hold the **ORBIT** tool in SteeringWheels and drag the cursor to display a view similar to the one specified for the project. Release the mouse button when the appropriate view is displayed, refer to Figure 14-13. Press ESC to exit.

6. In the **Project Browser**, right-click on {**3D**} under **3D Views** and rename {**3D**} to **Orthographic View** by using the **Rename** option from the shortcut menu displayed.

7. Double-click on **First Floor** in the **Floor Plans** head of the **Project Browser** to open corresponding floor plan in the drawing window.

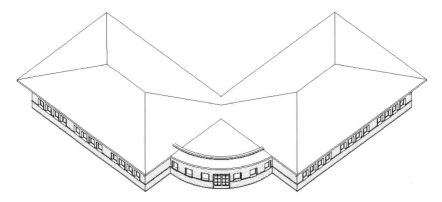

Figure 14-13 *Orthographic view of the Club project*

Saving the Project

In this section, you will save the project file using the **Save As** tool.

1. Choose **Save As > Project** from the **File** menu; the **Save As** dialog box is displayed.

2. Enter **c14_Club_tut2** in the **File name** edit box and choose **Save** to save the project file.

3. Choose **Close** from the **File** menu to close the project file.

EXERCISES

Exercise 1   Apartment 1

In this exercise, display the 3D exterior views using the file *c14-revit-2019-exr01.rvt* (for Metric *M_c14-revit-2019-exr01.rvt*) after downloading it from the CADSoft website *www.cadsofttech.com*. Create two exterior perspective views, one from the front and the other from the side of the building model, as shown in Figures 14-14 and 14-15, respectively. Use an appropriate camera location, target point, eye elevation, and target elevation to achieve the given perspective view.

(Expected time: 30 min)

Save the file as *c14_Apartment-1_ex1.rvt* (for Metric *M_c14_Apartment-1_ex1.rvt*)

Figure 14-14 3D exterior front view for Exercise 1

Figure 14-15 3D exterior side view for Exercise 1

Exercise 2   Office Building 1

In this exercise, display a 3D exterior front view using the file *c14-revit-2019-exr02.rvt* (for Metric *M_c14-revit-2019-exr02.rvt*) after downloading it from the CADSoft website *www.cadsofttech.com*, as shown in Figure 14-16. Use an appropriate camera location, target point, eye elevation, and target elevation to achieve the given perspective view.   (**Expected time: 15 min**)

Save the file as *c14_Office-1_ex2.rvt* (for Metric *M_c14_Office-1_ex2.rvt*)

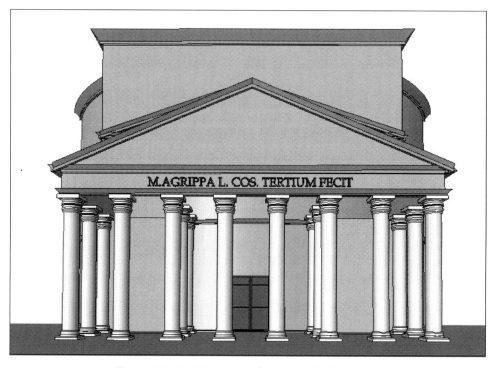

Figure 14-16 *3D exterior front view for Exercise 2*

Chapter 15

Rendering Views and Creating Walkthroughs

Learning Objectives

After completing this chapter, you will be able to:

- *Create a rendered scene*
- *Set natural and artificial lighting*
- *Create and render a walkthrough*
- *Know about Autodesk 360 / Rendering*

RENDERING IN REVIT

Rendering is a process of generating digital image from a three-dimensional model containing geometry, texture, light, and shading information through a computer program.

The rendering process helps you give a clear picture of the final outcome of an architectural project that you are working on. It bridges the gap between the final outcome and the two-dimensional working drawing, thereby giving you and your client the freedom to select the final finish with reduced cycle time for the approval and finalization of the design. Also, rendering with its rich photorealistic images helps you generate the actual bill of material for a project.

As described in the previous chapter, creating three-dimensional views of a building model enables you to visualize the interior and exterior of a building. However, to give a realistic effect to the view, it is necessary to apply materials to the building elements and render the view. The rendered exterior views of a building not only depict its overall scale, shape, and volume, but also represent the proposed exterior finish as envisaged by the architect. Similarly, a rendered interior three-dimensional view can be used to represent various interior elements such as interior partitions, furniture, plants, and interior finishes.

Rendering Workflow

In this chapter, you will learn about various methods and techniques used in a rendering workflow. A rendering workflow is a process chart that shows the flow of the rendering process to achieve the end result in the form of high quality rendered image, refer to Figure 15-1.

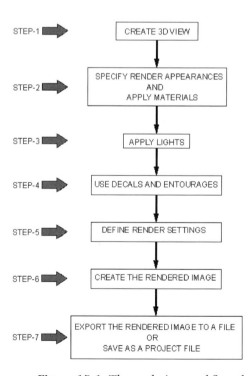

Figure 15-1 *The rendering workflow chart*

CREATING A WALKTHROUGH

A well rendered walkthrough can make a project presentation impressive. Using the **Walkthrough** tool, you can easily generate a walkthrough for a building model by rendering a series of 3D views defined by camera frames. The process of generating a walkthrough involves specifying a walkthrough path, editing it, and finally recording the walkthrough.

Creating the Walkthrough Path

Ribbon: View > Create > 3D View drop-down > Walkthrough

 The first step for creating a walkthrough is to define the walkthrough path that a camera follows through the building model. In most cases, this path is defined in the plan view. But, you can also use the section, elevation, and 3D views to define the path.

The walkthrough path is defined by specifying the points that form a spline in the project view. The specified points become key frames in the walkthrough. Autodesk Revit automatically generates additional intermediate frames between these key frames.

AUTODESK 360 | RENDERING

Autodesk 360 | Rendering is a cloud based rendering service that helps you to create photorealistic images and panoramic views for your project. It is a user interactive platform that provides a broad set of features including online cloud services, and related products.

The main features of the **Autodesk 360 | Rendering** service are:

1. Using the **Autodesk 360 | Rendering** service, you can render your Revit projects from any computer.

2. Using the **Autodesk 360 | Rendering** service, you can access multiple versions of your renderings, render images as panoramas, change rendering quality, and apply background environments to rendered scenes.

3. Using this service, the design files can be reviewed even without the Revit software by accessing the **Autodesk @ 360** account online or even on mobile applications. The design files can be shared among users and the file updates and e-mail notifications reach the users whenever the file is edited.

4. The rendered views generated by the **Autodesk 360 | Rendering** application are grouped as collection in the render gallery. You can also create and view panoramic views. Panoramic views can be accessed from the render gallery.

5. Using the **Autodesk 360 | Rendering** service, you can adjust the exposure of the rendered image directly without having to re-render from the original desktop application.

6. The **Autodesk 360 | Rendering** service helps you to preview the rendered image of a single day or multi-day solar studies.

TUTORIALS

Tutorial 1   Apartment 1

Using the project file *c14_Apartment1_tut1.rvt,* created in Tutorial 1 of Chapter 14, render the interior view of the living room at first floor, as shown in Figure 15-2. Replace the existing finish of materials assigned to the floor, wall, ceiling, and chair with new materials/textures (given with their path). Also, create a 200-frame interior walkthrough at eye level using the path shown in Figure 15-3.   **(Expected time: 1 hr)**

The rendered image can be downloaded from *http://www.cadsofttech.com.* The path of the file is as follows: *Textbooks > Civil/GIS > Revit Architecture > Revit Architecture 2019 For Novices*

Note
The expected time of completing the tutorial does not include the rendering time. The rendering time will depend upon the system configuration.

Figure 15-2 The interior view of the living room after rendering

The materials used for rendering the scene are as follows:

1. New material for walls: **Finishes - Interior - Gypsum Wall Board** with **Wall-Paint Matte** render appearance.
2. New material for ceiling: **Finishes - Interior - Gypsum Wall Board - Ceiling**
3. New material for floor: **Vinyl Composition Tile**
4. New cushion material for **Chair Corbu: Textile - Brown Leather**

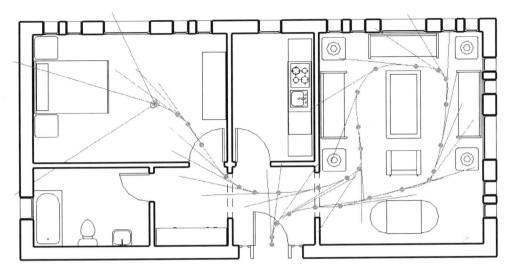

Figure 15-3 *Sketch plan showing the walkthrough path for the Apartment 1 project*

Add lights based on the parameters given next, refer to Figures 15-4 and 15-5. The exact location of lights is not important in this tutorial.

1.   Light Fixtures to be loaded and used from the **US Imperial > Lighting Fixture** folder:
    Table Lamp - Standard
    Pendant Light - Disk

The following steps are required to complete this tutorial:

a.   Open the specified project file and the first floor plan view.

b.   Apply materials to the floor using the **Paint** tool.

c.   Change the finish of the ceiling, walls, and textile of the chair using the **Material Browser** dialog box.

d.   Load lighting fixtures and add them to the floor and ceiling plan, refer to Figures 15-6 through 15-11.

e.   Add RPC to the view, refer to Figures 15-12 and 15-13.

f.   Set the rendering scene and generate the rendered image, refer to Figure 15-14.

g.   Specify the walkthrough path and create a walkthrough, refer to Figures 15-15 through 15-16.

h.   Save the project using the **Save As** tool.

      For Imperial   *c15_Apartment1_tut1.rvt*
      For Metric   *M_c15_Apartment1_tut1.rvt*

i.   Close the project.

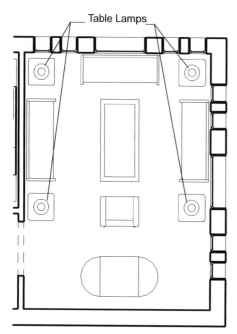

Table Lamps

Pendant Light - Disk

Figure 15-4 *Sketch floor plan for adding table lamps to the living room*

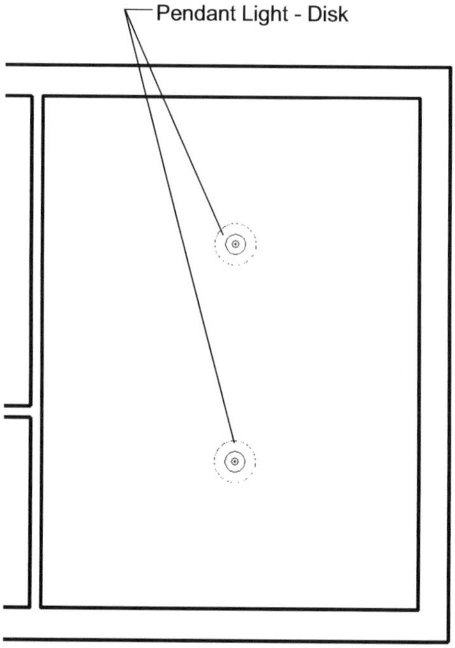

Figure 15-5 *Sketch ceiling plan for adding ceiling lights to the living room*

Opening the Project File and the First Floor Plan View

1. Choose **Open > Project** from the **File** menu and then open the *c14_Apartment1_tut1.rvt* for imperial and *M_c14_Apartment1_tut1.rvt* for metric file created in Tutorial 1 of Chapter 14. You can also download this file from *http://www.cadsofttech.com*. The path of the file is as follows: *Textbooks > Civil/GIS > Revit Architecture > Revit Architecture 2019 For Novices*.

2. Now, double-click on **First Floor** in the **Floor Plans** head of the **Project Browser** to open the corresponding floor plan in the drawing window.

    As dimensions and tags are not required for this tutorial, you can turn off their visibility by using the **Visibility/ Graphics** tool.

3. Choose the **Visibility/ Graphics** tool from the **Graphics** panel of the **View** tab; the **Visibility/Graphic Overrides for Floor Plan: First Floor** dialog box is displayed. Choose the **Annotation Categories** tab and clear the check boxes for **Callouts**, **Dimensions**, **Furniture Tags**, and **Room Tags**.

4. Next, choose the **Apply** button and then the **OK** button to view the changes in the drawing area and to close the dialog box, respectively.

Modifying the Floor Material Using the Paint Tool

In this section of the tutorial, you will modify the finishes of the materials used in the building model. Also, you will use the **Paint** tool to apply the material to the floor in the section view.

1. Double-click on **Section X** under the **Sections (Building Section)** head in the **Project Browser** to display the section in the drawing window.

2. Choose the **Paint** tool from **Modify > Geometry > Paint** drop-down; the **Material Browser <default material name>** dialog box is displayed.

3. In the **Search** edit box of the **Material Browser** dialog box, type the **Vinyl Composition Tile** for Imperial and **Birch** for Metric; the corresponding material is displayed in the **Project Materials: All** area.

4. Select the **Vinyl Composition Tile** material.

5. Now, in the drawing area, move the cursor near the top of the floor at the **First Floor** level in the section view and click when it is highlighted; the selected material is applied to the floor top. Choose the **Done** button in the **Material Browser** dialog box to close the dialog box.

Modifying the Finish of the Materials Using the Material Editor

In this section, you will modify the finish of other elements by using the **Material Browser** dialog box.

1. Choose the **Modify** button from the **Select** panel and then move the cursor over the left exterior wall. Next, click to select the wall when it is highlighted.

2. Now, choose the **Type Properties** button in the **Properties** panel of the **Modify | Walls** tab; the **Type Properties** dialog box is displayed.

3. Next, choose the **Edit** button in the **Value** column for the **Structure** parameter to display the **Edit Assembly** dialog box, refer to Figure 15-6.

The finishes and structure of the selected wall type are displayed in the **Layers** area and are arranged with the exterior finish as the first and the interior finish as the last layer, refer to Figure 15-6. As the material properties of the interior finish need to be modified, you will modify the last layer (**Finish 2 [5]**).

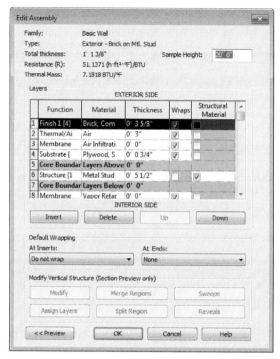

*Figure 15-6 The **Edit Assembly** dialog box for the exterior wall type*

4. Click in the **Material** column for the **Finish 2 [5]** layer and choose the browse button; the **Material Browser** dialog box along with the **Material Editor** pane is displayed.

5. In the **Material Browser** dialog box, ensure that the **Gypsum Wall Board** option is selected in the **Project Materials: All** area and its parameters are displayed in the **Material Editor** pane.

6. Choose the **Appearance** tab; the preview of the selected material and its properties are displayed. Now, choose the **Replaces this asset** button from this tab; the **Asset Browser** dialog box is displayed, as shown in Figure 15-7.

7. In the **Asset Browser** dialog box, choose **Appearance Library > Wall Paint > Matte > Biege** from **Appearance Library**; a double arrow button is displayed.

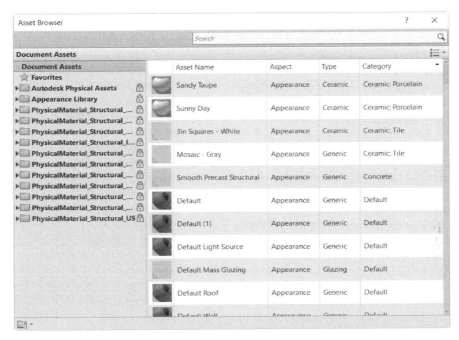

Figure 15-7 *The **Asset Browser** dialog box*

8. Choose the **Replaces the current asset in the editor with this asset** button to replace the current asset from the selected option. Close the **Asset Browser** dialog box and then choose the **OK** button in the **Material Browser** dialog box; the **Material Browser** dialog box along with the **Material Editor** pane is closed.

9. Close all the dialog boxes and return to the drawing window. Now, press ESC to exit the selection.

   Next, modify the appearance of the ceiling material.

10. Open the first floor ceiling plan and select it; the **Modify | Multi-Select** tab is displayed. Choose the **Filter** tool from the **Selection** panel of this contextual tab; the **Filter** dialog box is displayed. By default, all the check boxes are selected. Clear all the check boxes except the check box corresponding to the **Ceilings** parameter.

11. Choose the **OK** button; the **Filter** dialog box is closed; the **Modify | Ceilings** contextual tab is displayed.

12. Now, choose the **Type Properties** tool from the **Properties** panel of the **Modify | Ceilings** tab; the **Type Properties** dialog box is displayed.

13. Choose the **Edit** button in the **Value** field of the **Structure** parameter; the **Edit Assembly** dialog box is displayed with different layers of the selected ceiling.

14. Click in the **Material** column, the **Finish 2 [5]** layer for Imperial and **Structure[1]** for Metric, and then choose the browse button to display the **Material Browser** dialog box.

15. In the **Material Browser** dialog box, the **Gypsum Wall Board** option is selected in the **Project Materials: All** area. The **Material Editor** pane displays the properties of material. Choose the **Duplicate Selected Material** option from the **Creates and duplicates materials** drop-down list located at the lower left corner of the **Material Browser** dialog box; the name **Gypsum Wall Board(1)** is displayed in the **Name** edit box of the **Identity** tab in the **Material Browser** dialog box. Enter the name **Finish - Interior - Gypsum Wall Board - Ceiling** in this edit box.

16. Now, choose the **Replaces this asset** button from the **Appearance** tab; the **Asset Browser** dialog box is displayed. In this dialog box, choose **Paint > Glossy > Paint - Enamel Glossy (White)** from **Appearance Library**. Click on double-arrow button to replace the current asset.

17. Close the **Asset Browser** dialog box. Choose the **Apply** button and then the **OK** button to close the **Material Browser** dialog box. Choose the **OK** button in the **Edit Assembly** and the **Type Properties** dialog boxes to close them.

    Next, you will modify the texture of the chair textile.

18. Open the first floor plan view in the drawing window using the **Project Browser**.

19. Select the **Chair-Corbu** for Imperial (**M_Chair-Corbo** for Metric) in the living room and then choose the **Edit Type** button from the **Properties** palette; the **Type Properties** dialog box is displayed.

20. In this dialog box, click in the **Value** column for the **Cushion Material** type parameter and choose the browse button; the **Material Browser** dialog box is displayed.

21. In the **Material Browser** dialog box, choose the **Duplicate Selected Material** option from the **Creates and Duplicates Materials** drop-down list at the lower left corner of the **Material Browser** dialog box. Enter the name **Textile - Brown Leather** in the **Name** edit box and press ENTER.

22. Choose the **Replaces this asset** button from the **Appearance** tab in the **Material Editor** pane; the **Asset Browser** dialog box is displayed. In the **Asset Browser** dialog box, choose **Fabric > Leather** option from the **Appearance Library**.

23. Next, select the **Brown** material in the right pane of the **Appearance Library** area and click on the double arrow button to replace the current asset.

24. Now, close the **Asset Browser** dialog box and choose the **Graphics** tab from the **Materials Browser** dialog box; the **Graphic Properties** will be displayed in the **Material Editor** pane. Select the **Use Render Appearance** check box in the **Shading** area and then choose the **OK** button in the **Material Browser** and the **Type Properties** dialog boxes to close them. Now, press ESC to exit the selection of the chair. The **Leather** material are assigned to the chair.

Loading and Adding Light Fixtures to the Building Model

In this section of the tutorial, you will load the light fixtures and then add them to the floor and ceiling plan.

1. Choose the **Place a Component** tool from **Architecture > Build > Component** drop-down; the **Modify | Place Component** tab is displayed.

2. Now, choose the **Load Family** tool from the **Mode** panel; the **Load Family** dialog box is displayed.

3. Navigate through the **US Imperial > Lighting > Architectural > Internal** folder and load the **Table Lamp - Standard** and **Pendant Light - Disk** for Imperial (**US Metric > Lighting > Architectural > Internal** folder and load the M_**Table Lamp - Standard** and M_**Pendant Light - Disk** for Metric) fixtures using the CTRL key. Choose the **Open** button to return to the drawing area.

4. From the **Type Selector** drop-down list, select the **Table Lamp-Standard : 60W - 120V** fixture.

5. Move the cursor near the center of the side table placed at the lower right of the living room and click when the **Midpoint and Midpoint** object snap is displayed, as shown in Figure 15-8. Now, choose the **Modify** button to exit the selection mode.

6. Next, select the added table lamp; instance parameters for the component are displayed in the **Properties** palette.

7. Enter the value **1'3"** for Imperial (**381mm** for Metric) in the value column for the **Offset** instance parameter and then choose the **Apply** button.

8. Use the **Copy** tool in the **Modify** panel to copy the added lamp on the other three side tables, as shown in Figure 15-9 (Select the **Multiple** check box in the **Options Bar**). Now, press ESC twice to exit the current selection.

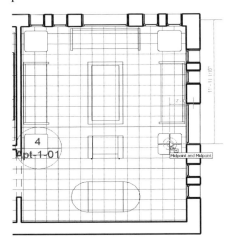

Figure 15-8 *Adding lamp to the side table*

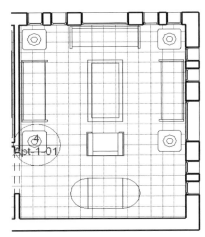

Figure 15-9 *Creating multiple copies of the table lamp component*

9.   Double-click on **First Floor** under the **Ceiling Plans** head in the **Project Browser** to display the ceiling plan view.

10. Next, choose the **Place a Component** tool from the **Architecture > Build > Component** drop-down; the **Modify | Place Component** tab is displayed. Select the **Pendant Light - Disk: 100W - 120V** fixture from the **Type Selector** drop-down list.

11. Move the cursor over the sitting area in the living room and click to add the light fixture at the approximate location, as shown in Figure 15-10.

12. Similarly, add the same fixture to the other side of the living room, as shown in Figure 15-11 and then press ESC twice to exit the **Modify | Place Component** tab.

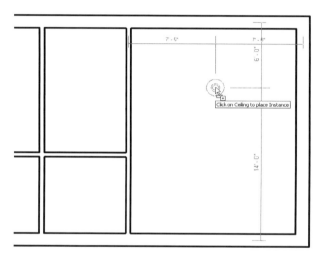

Figure 15-10 *Adding the first light fixture in the ceiling plan*

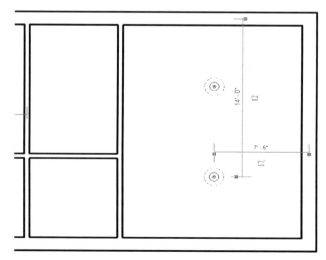

Figure 15-11 *Adding the second light fixture in the ceiling plan*

Adding RPC to the Interior Scene

In this section of the tutorial, you will use the **Place a Component** tool to load and add the specified RPC to the interior scene. The specified RPC (Rich Photorealistic Content) can be added at the location shown in Figure 15-12.

1. Open the first floor plan view from the **Floor Plans** heading in the drawing window using the **Project Browser**.

2. Now, choose the **Place a Component** tool from the **Architecture > Build > Component** drop-down; the **Modify | Place Component** tab is displayed.

3. Choose the **Load Family** tool from the **Mode** panel; the **Load Family** dialog box is displayed.

4. Navigate through the **US Imperial > Entourage** folder, select the **RPC Female** for Imperial (**US Metric > Entourage** folder, select the **M_RPC Female** for Metric) family file and then choose **Open**; the selected family file is now loaded.

5. Next, select the **RPC Female : Cynthia** option from the **Type Selector** drop-down list.

6. Now, select the **Rotate after placement** check box from the **Options Bar** and then click on the sofa and move the cursor counterclockwise. Next, click to place and align the RPC in the view, as shown in Figure 15-12.

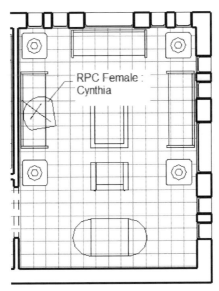

Figure 15-12 RPC added to the view

7. Press the ESC key twice to exit the insertion process. Double-click on **Living Area** under the **3D Views** head in the **Project Browser** to view the 3D view after adding the lighting fixtures and RPC, refer to Figure 15-13.

8. Choose **Visual Style > Shaded** from **View Control Bar**; the current view will be shaded.

 Note
You can set the position of the RPCs by selecting the required elevation or section views from the ***Project Browser***.

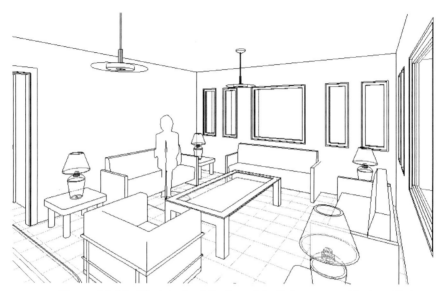

Figure 15-13 *The interior 3D view of the living room with the added lighting fixtures and RPC*

Setting Up the Interior Rendering Scene

In this section of the tutorial, you will invoke the **Rendering** dialog box and specify the settings to render the interior scene.

1. Invoke the **Rendering** dialog box by choosing the **Show Rendering Dialog** button from **View Control Bar**. Alternatively, you can press RR to display the **Rendering** dialog box.

2. In the **Quality** area of the **Rendering** dialog box, select the **Best** option from the **Setting** drop-down list.

3. In the **Lighting** area, select the **Interior : Sun and Artificial** option from the **Scheme** drop-down list.

4. Choose the Browse button displayed next to the **Sun Setting** text box; the **Sun Settings** dialog box is displayed.

5. Select the **Still** radio button in the **Solar Study** area.

6. Choose the button next to the **Location** parameter in the **Settings** area to invoke the **Location Weather and Site** dialog box.

7. In the **Location** tab, select the **Default City List** option from the **Define Location by** drop-down list. Select **Chicago, IL** from the **City** drop-down list and choose the **OK** button.

8. Set the date **14/06/2019** in the **Date** drop-down list and then set the time to **10:00 PM** in the **Time** spinner.

9. Clear the **Ground Plane at Level** check box, if selected.

10. Choose **Apply** and **OK**; the specified settings are applied to the scene and the **Sun Settings** dialog box is closed.

11. Next, in the **Image** area of the **Rendering** dialog box, choose the **Adjust Exposure** button to invoke the **Exposure Control** dialog box.

12. In the **Exposure Control** dialog box, set the values of the parameters as given below:

   Exposure Value: **6.5**   Highlights: **0.45**
   Saturation: **1**   Shadows: **0.2**
   White Point: **4000**

13. Choose **Apply** and **OK**; the specified settings are applied to the scene and the **Exposure Control** dialog box is closed.

14. In the **Rendering** dialog box, choose the **Render** button; Autodesk Revit starts the rendering process using the mental ray rendering engine for the interior view. The **Rendering Progress** dialog box is displayed on your screen. On completion of the process, the rendered image is displayed in the drawing area, as shown in Figure 15-14.

15. After the rendering process is complete, choose the **Save to Project** button in the **Image** area; the **Save to Project** dialog box is displayed. Enter **Living Area** in the **Name** edit box and choose the **OK** button. This will add the rendered image under the **Renderings** head in the **Project Browser**. Now, close the **Rendering** dialog box.

   The rendered image can be downloaded from *http://www.cadsofttech.com*. The path of the file is as follows: *Textbooks > Civil/GIS > Revit Architecture > Revit Architecture 2019 For Novices*.

 Note
*Depending on the hardware configuration of the system, it might take considerable time to render. To do a quick render, select **Draft** or **Low** from the **Setting** drop-down list in the **Rendering** dialog box.*

Figure 15-14 The interior 3D view of the living room rendered using mental ray

Generating the Walkthrough

In this section, you will specify the walkthrough path in the floor plan view.

1. Double-click on **First Floor** under the **Floor Plans** head in the **Project Browser**.

2. Choose the **Walkthrough** tool from the **View > Create > 3D View** drop-down; the **Modify | Walkthrough** tab is displayed. Note that the cursor changes into a **+** mark and different options related to creating a walkthrough path are displayed in the **Options Bar**.

3. Now, start sketching the walkthrough path by clicking at the first point near the center of the main entrance door of the apartment. Ensure that the first point is specified inside the lobby area and not outside the entrance door. Move the cursor toward the living room and click to specify multiple points in such a manner that they form a counterclockwise loop around the center table in the living room, as shown in Figure 15-15.

4. Similarly, move the cursor across the lobby and inside the bed room. Next, click to specify multiple points of the walkthrough path, refer to Figure 15-15. The exact location of these points is not critical.

5. After specifying the last point, choose the **Finish Walkthrough** button from the **Walkthrough** panel of the **Modify | Walkthrough** tab; walkthrough path is now completed and the **Modify | Cameras** tab is displayed.

Note

The dots indicate the specified points and are shown only for illustration. They are not displayed when the walkthrough path is being specified.

Note that the generated walkthrough is now added to the **Project Browser** as **Walkthrough 1** under the new **Walkthroughs** head. You can now modify the total frames for the walkthrough using the **Edit Walkthrough** button.

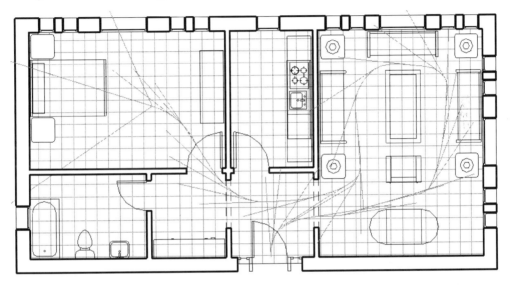

Figure 15-15 Sketch plan showing the walkthrough path for the Apartment 1 project

6. Double-click on **Walkthrough 1** under the **Walkthroughs** head in the **Project Browser**. Choose the **Edit Walkthrough** button from the **Walkthrough** panel of the **Modify | Cameras** tab; the **Edit Walkthrough** contextual tab is displayed.

7. In the **Options Bar**, ensure that the **Active Camera** option is selected from the **Controls** drop-down list and **200** is displayed in the **Frame** edit box. Now, choose the **Frame Settings** button next to the **Frame** edit box; the **Walkthrough Frames** dialog box is displayed.

8. In the **Walkthrough Frames** dialog box, enter **200** as the value in the **Total Frames** edit box and choose the **OK** button; the specified settings are now assigned to the walkthrough and the **Walkthrough Frames** dialog box closes. Also the total number of frames in the walkthrough gets modified from **300** to **200** as specified for this tutorial.

Recording the Walkthrough

In this section of the tutorial, you will open the walkthrough, adjust the field of view of the camera and then record it by exporting it using the **AVI** file format.

1. In the **Options Bar**, enter **1** in the **Frame** edit box. Now, choose the **Edit Walkthrough** tab and then choose the **Open Walkthrough** button from the **Walkthrough** panel. The first frame is opened in the drawing window.

2. Right-click inside the drawing window and choose **Zoom Out (2x)** from the shortcut menu displayed.

3. Drag the extents of the rectangle to modify the field of view for the camera such that the view resembles the illustration given in Figure 15-16.

4. Right-click again and choose **Zoom To Fit** to enlarge the view.

5. Next, you will export the walkthrough as an AVI file.

    From the **File** menu, choose **Export > Images and Animations > Walkthrough**; the **Length Format** dialog box is displayed, as shown in Figure 15-17.

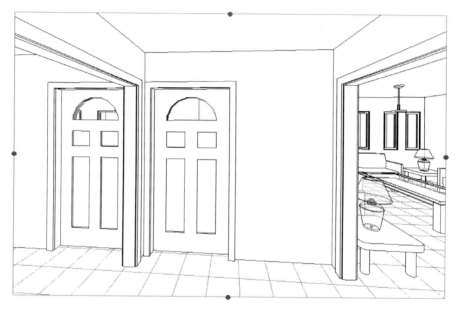

Figure 15-16 First frame of the walkthrough with the modified field of view

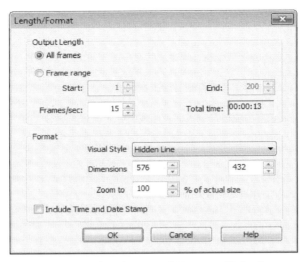

*Figure 15-17 The **Length/Format** dialog box*

6. In the **Length/Format** dialog box, ensure that the **All frames** radio button is selected and then set **10** in the **Frames/sec** spinner.

7. In the **Format** area, select **Rendering** from the **Visual Style** drop-down list.

8. Next, set the value in the **Zoom to** spinner to **43** and choose the **OK** button; the **Length/ Format** dialog box closes and the **Export Walkthrough** dialog box is displayed.

9. In the **Export Walkthrough** dialog box, specify an appropriate path, enter **c15_Apartment1_ tut1_Walkthrough 1** for Imperial and **M_c15_Apartment_tut1_ Walkthrough 1** for Metric in the **File name** edit box, and then make sure that AVI Files is the default file format selected in the **Files of type** drop-down list. Now, choose the **Save** button; the rendering and recording process starts. After rendering of the first frame, the **Video Compression** dialog box gets displayed. Keep the **Full Frames (Uncompressed)** option selected in the **Compressor** drop-down list and choose the OK button to continue.

    Now, the rendering and recording process starts for each frame of the walkthrough and the **Rendering Progress** dialog box is displayed. When the procedure is completed, the file is recorded at the specified location. You can then use any media player to view the walkthrough file.

Saving the Project

In this section, you will save the project file using the **Save As** tool.

1. Choose **Save As > Project** from the **File** menu; the **Save As** dialog box is displayed.

2. Enter **c15_Apartment1_tut1** for Imperial and **M_ c15_Apartment1_tut1** for Metric in the **File name** edit box and then choose **Save**.

3. Choose **Close** from the **File** menu to close the project file.

Tutorial 2   Office Building 2

Render the exterior view of the *Office Building 2* project using the file created in Exercise 3 of Chapter 14. Replace the existing finishes of materials assigned to the exterior walls with the new materials/textures, add trees, and add entourages to the project based on the first floor plan view, as shown in Figure 15-18. Render the 3D view 1 based on the rendered view shown in Figure 15-19.   **(Expected time: 30 min)**

The rendered image can be downloaded from *http://www.cadsofttech.com*. The path of the file is as follows: *Textbooks > Civil/GIS > Revit Architecture > Revit Architecture 2019 For Novices*
1. New material for the exterior wall finish: **Finishes - Exterior- Cladding**
2. New material for toposurface: **Site - Grass**
3. Trees to be loaded and used from **US Imperial\Planting\RPC Tree - Deciduous**

The following steps are required to complete this tutorial:

a. Open the specified project file and the first floor plan view.
b. Apply materials to the exterior walls using the **Paint** tool.
c. Add a toposurface to the building model and assign material to it.
d. Add trees to the exterior view.
e. Add entourages to the building model.
f. Set up the rendering scene and render.
g. Save the project using the **Save As** tool.
       For Imperial   *c15_Office-2_tut2.rvt*
       For Metric   *M_c15_Office-2_tut2.rvt*
h. Close the project.

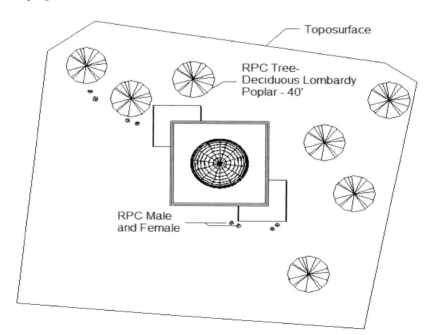

Figure 15-18   *Sketch plan for adding toposurface, trees, and entourages to the Office Building 2*

Figure 15-19 Rendered exterior view for Office Building 2 project

Opening the Project File and the First Floor Plan View

1. To open the specified file
    Choose **Open > Project** from the **File** menu and then open the *c14_Office-2_ex3.rvt* file created in Exercise 3 of Chapter14. You can also download this file from *http://www.cadsofttech.com*. The path of the file is as follows: *Textbooks > Civil/GIS > Revit Architecture > Revit Architecture 2019 For Novices*

2. Double-click on **First Floor** in the **Floor Plans** head of the **Project Browser** to open the corresponding floor plan in the drawing window.

Modifying the Finishes of the Exterior Wall Using the Paint Tool

In this section of the tutorial, you will first create a new material and then use the **Paint** tool to apply it over the exterior walls.

1. Choose the **Materials** tool from the **Settings** panel of the **Manage** tab; the **Material Browser** dialog box is displayed.

2. In the **Material Browser** dialog box, double-click on the **Metal Deck** from the **Project Materials: All** area; the **Material Editor** pane displays properties of **Metal Deck**. In this dialog box, choose the **Duplicate Selected Material** tool from the **Creates and duplicates Materials** drop-down; a duplicate material name will be displayed in the edit box.

3. In the edit box, enter **Finishes-Exterior-Cladding** and choose the **Appearance** tab in the **Editor** pane. Choose the **Replaces this asset** button; the **Asset Browser** dialog box is displayed.

4. Expand **Appearance Library** in the **Assets Browser** dialog box and choose **Masonry > Brick** from the expanded list.

5. Next, choose the **Non-Uniform Running - Red** material from the material list in the right pane of the **Asset Browser** dialog box and click on the double arrow button to assign the material.

6. Now, close the **Asset Browser** dialog box and you can see the updated preview in the material preview box.

7. Next, choose the **Graphics** tab then select the **Use Render Appearance** check box in the **Shading** Area. Choose the **Apply** and **OK** buttons; the **Material Browser** dialog box is closed.

   You can now use the **Paint** tool to apply the created texture to the exterior walls.

8. Use the **Zoom in Region** tool from the **Navigation Bar** to enlarge the main building in the first floor plan.

9. Now, choose the **Paint** tool from the **Modify > Geometry > Paint** drop-down; the **Modify | Paint** tab and the **Materials Browser** dialog box are displayed.

10. From this dialog box, select the **Finishes - Exterior-Cladding** material.

11. In the drawing area, move the cursor over the exterior face of the wall of the center building; the face gets highlighted. Next, click on the highlighted exterior face; the selected material gets applied to it.

12. Apply the selected texture to the exterior faces of the other exterior walls that are visible in the plan view and then choose the **Done** button in the **Materials Browser** dialog box to close it.

   You can open the 3D view and then choose **Visual Style > Shaded** from the **View Control Bar**, if it is not selected, to display the shaded view of the modified exterior finish. Then, return to the plan view.

Creating a Toposurface and Adding Material to It

In this section of the tutorial, you will create a toposurface to add a base to the building and then add a material to it.

1. Double-click on **Site** in the **Floor Plans** head of the **Project Browser** to open the site plan. Now, hide the elevation symbol by using the **Visibility/ Graphics** tool from the **View** tab.

2. Next, choose the **Massing & Site** tab and then choose the **Toposurface** tool from the **Model Site** panel; the **Modify | Edit Surface** contextual tab is displayed.

3. Now, add points to the drawing area to create the toposurface, refer to Figure 15-18.

Note
The size of the toposurface can vary and is based on the extent of its visibility in the 3D view.

4. Next, choose the **Finish Surface** button from the **Surface** panel of the **Modify | Edit Surface** tab. Next, select the toposurface so that the instance parameters for the surface are displayed in the **Properties** palette.

5. Click on the value field of the **Material** parameter and then choose the browse button to display the **Materials Browser** dialog box.

6. In the dialog box, choose the **Earth** option from the **Project Material: All** list area.

7. Choose the **Duplicate Selected Material** option from the **Creates and duplicates materials** drop-down at the lower left corner of the **Material Browser** dialog box; the name **Earth(1)** is displayed in the list under the **Project Material: All** area. Enter the name **Site - Grass** in the **Name** edit box of the **Identity** tab.

8. Choose the **Replaces this asset** button in the **Appearance** tab; the **Asset browser** dialog box is displayed. Now, expand the **Appearance Library** in the left pane of the **Asset Browser** dialog box and select **Sitework > Grass - Bermuda**. Next, click on the double arrow button to update the material.

9. Next, close the **Asset Browser** dialog box to return to the **Material Browser** dialog box. Choose the **Graphics** tab from this dialog box; the graphic properties of the material gets displayed. Select the **Use Render Appearance** check box in the **Shading** area and then choose the **Apply** and **OK** buttons in the **Material Browser** dialog box.

10. Now, press ESC to exit the selection.

    You will now use the **Site Component** tool to load and add the specified planting elements and people to the building model. The trees and people can be added to the location given in the sketch plan, refer to Figure 15-18.

11. Next, choose the **Site Component** tool from the **Model Site** panel of the **Massing & Site** tab; the **Modify | Site Component** tab is displayed.

12. Now, choose the **Load Family** tool from the **Mode** panel; the **Load Family** dialog box is displayed.

13. Navigate through the **US Imperial > Planting** folder and select **RPC Tree - Deciduous** (**US Metric > Planting** folder and select **M_RPC Tree - Deciduous**) and then choose the **Open** button; the selected family type is loaded.

14. Now, from the **Type Selector** drop-down list in the **Properties** pallete, select **RPC Tree - Deciduous : Lombardy Poplar - 40'** for Imperial (**M_RPC Tree - Deciduous : Lombardy Poplar - 12.2 Meters** for Metric).

15. Move the cursor near the location shown in the sketch plan for this tutorial and click to add the planting element.

Similarly, click again at the diagonally opposite corners of the office building to add another instance of the planting element based on the given sketch plan. Further add more planting elements, refer to Figure 15-18.

16. Next, to add people to the building model, repeat steps 11 and 12 and invoke the **Load Family** dialog box.

17. Navigate through the **US Imperial > Entourage** folder and load the **RPC Male** and **RPC Female** families for Imperial (**US Metric > Entourage** folder and load the **M_RPC Male** and **M_RPC Female** families for Metric).

18. From the **Type Selector** drop-down list in the Properties pallete, select **RPC Male : Jay**, **RPC Male : Dwayne**, **RPC Male : LaRon**, **RPC Male : Alex**, **RPC Female : Cathy**, **RPC Female : YinYin**, **RPC Female : Tina**, and **RPC Female : Lisa** individually and then add them to the building model as per the site plan, refer to Figure 15-18.

Note
The locations of the RPCs are not fixed. You can change them according to the clarity of view and the requirement of the image.

Setting Up the Exterior Rendering Scene

You will now provide the information required to set up the rendering scene. To make the rendering tools available, open the 3D view of the project.

1. Open the {3D} view from the **3D Views** head in the **Project Browser**.

2. Choose the **Show Rendering Dialog** button from the **View Control Bar** to invoke the **Rendering** dialog box.

3. In the **Quality** area of the **Rendering** dialog box, select the **Best** option from the **Setting** drop-down list. Select the **Screen** radio button in the **Resolution** area, if it is not selected.

Note
*The rendering process may take considerable time if you select the **Best** option from the **Settings** drop-down list. To render quickly, select the **Low** or **Draft** option from the **Settings** drop-down list in the **Rendering** dialog box.*

4. Select the **Exterior: Sun only** option from the **Scheme** drop-down list in the **Lighting** area.

5. Next, in this area, choose the Browse button from the **Sun Setting** drop-down list to display the **Sun Settings** dialog box.

6. In the **Solar Study** area of the **Sun Settings** dialog box, ensure that the **Lighting** radio button is selected.

7. Ensure that **135.00°** is displayed in the **Azimuth** edit box. Next, enter **60.00°** in the **Altitude** edit box and then choose the **OK** button; the **Rendering** dialog box is displayed.

8. In the **Background** area, select the **Sky: Few Clouds** option from the **Style** drop-down list.

Rendering the Exterior View

In this section of the tutorial, you will render the exterior view using the mental ray rendering engine.

1. In the **Rendering** dialog box, choose the **Render** button to start the rendering process.

2. When you finish the rendering process, choose the **Adjust Exposure** button in the **Image** area to invoke the **Exposure Control** dialog box.

3. Enter **13.5** in the **Exposure Value** edit box and **0.3** in the **Shadows** edit box.

4. Choose the **OK** button to return to the **Rendering** dialog box.

5. Choose the **Save to Project** button in the **Image** area; the **Save to Project** dialog box is displayed.

6. Enter the name of the rendered view as **Exterior View 1** in the **Name** edit box and choose the **OK** button to return to the **Rendering** dialog box. Next, close the **Rendering** dialog box. Now, expand the **Renderings** head in the **Project Browser** and double-click on the **Exterior View 1**; the rendered view is displayed in the drawing area.

7. After viewing the rendered image, double-click on **First Floor** under the **Floor Plans** head in the **Project Browser**.

Saving the Project

In this section, you will save the project file using the **Save As** tool.

1. Choose **Save As > Project** from the **File** menu; the **Save As** dialog box is displayed. Enter **c15_Office-2_tut2** for Imperial and **M_c15_Office-2_tut2** for Metric in the **File name** edit box and then choose **Save**; the project file is saved.

2. Choose **Close** from the **File** menu; the project file closes.

EXERCISES

Exercise 1   Club

Using the *c14_Club_tut2.rvt* project file created in Tutorial 2 of Chapter 14, render the entrance view, as shown in Figure 15-20. Assume all the information required for this exercise.
Save the file as *c15_Club_ex1.rvt*   **(Expected time: 30 min)**

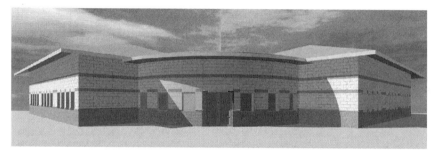

Figure 15-20 Rendered exterior view of the Club project

Exercise 2   Apartment 1 - Night View

Using the project file created in Tutorial 1 of this chapter, render the night scene of the living room, as shown in Figure 15-21. You need to modify the time settings to 6:00 A.M.
Save the file as *c15_Apartment-1_ex2.rvt*.   **(Expected time: 30 min)**

The rendered image can be downloaded from *http://www.cadsofttech.com*. The path of the file is as follows: *Textbooks > Civil/GIS > Revit Architecture > Revit Architecture 2019 For Novices*

Figure 15-21 Rendered interior view of the living room

Index

29432586R00165

Printed in Great Britain
by Amazon